THE HAPPY SADIST

THE HAPPY SADIST

Robert Newton Peck

Drawings by Raymond Davidson

DOUBLEDAY & COMPANY, INC.
GARDEN CITY, NEW YORK

All of the characters in this book
are fictitious, and any resemblance
to actual persons, living or dead,
is purely coincidental.

FOREWORD

Ever since I can remember, my goal was to become a happy sadist. A happy sadist, perhaps I should explain, is a balance between evil and wit, and his laugh, though warped, is not malicious. He is not the boob who paints a swastika on a temple. But he might pencil a tiny R$_x$ on a Christian Science church.[1]

Why such a goal? Certainly I owe you a truthful word of explanation before setting down my autobiography, which has been slightly fictionalized in the interests of truth, justice, and the libel laws.

Here we are, helpless in a society where shaving lather is extra wet and beer extra dry. We pride ourselves on having the same ratio, roughly 7 to 1, in our engine compression as in our martinis. We have wall-to-wall coffee tables, egg beaters with automatic transmission, six-month deodorants, five-day floor wax, can openers with power steering, squeeze-bottle flapjacks, and pens that write on butter. It's enough to wrap a man up in a little white jacket and march him off to the giggle gang singing the *Alfred Landon Victory March.* So, I'm revolting. And here's how it all began:

[1] Apologies to Mary Nelson Eddy.

FOREWORD

Back in the days when toothpaste was white and the White Sox were black, I was born around the corner from Hoover prosperity on a small farm in Weedville, New York. I say it was a farm, but my father had very little land and didn't have a cow, although we did have cows until I was eight years old. That was the year I secretly convinced our prize herd of Holsteins that they weren't cows at all, but were really lemmings, and one night they all stampeded into the brook to commit suicide. Funniest thing you ever saw.

Paw was annoyed at first until finally he saw the humor in it and then he laughed to beat hell. He even hummed a few bars of *I Must Go Down to the Sea Again* while he whopped the be-Jesus out of me.

Perhaps the reader at this point is beginning to think that happy sadism was all I ever aspired to. Nothing could be farther from the truth. I am not only a successful author and a svelte young advertising executive, but a song writer as well. In 1928, at the age of six months, I wrote my first popular song, *Good Luck in the White House, Al Smith.* I tried for years to get it published. No one would accept it because all music publishers were anti-Catholic until Billy Graham finally wrote *Going My Way.*

In biology class, the other students chose to dissect a frog. I just couldn't. Frogs, when you get to know them, are the most lovable, the most affectionate, and most intelligent friends that man has in the animal kingdom. Kill one, and dissect it? Never! Instead, I dissected Lucky, my dog. He was getting old anyhow. Our picture made the cover of *Vivisection Journal* and everyone remarked on it. I learned later that if you want a striking magazine cover to boost newsstand sales, a picture of a boy and his dog will do it every time.

As a dog-hater, the picture greatly amused my uncle Ned. Did I mention Ned earlier? He was not only a dog-hater, he was also a diabetic. He scoffed at the doctor's advice and one Sunday evening dropped dead watching the *Loretta Young Show*. All of us who survived mourned him for days. His was not a large family. The immediate survivors were only his wife—and a dog. For all his dog-hating, this was an animal he liked. Uncle Ned had married a French dentist with one of those charming continental names, Claire Tooth-Loose, a descendant of Henri Tooth-Loose LauTrec, the inventor of Bermuda shorts. Claire owned a giant St. Bernard dog named Id, who was raised in the Alps and would eat nothing but frozen monks.

Feeding old Id became quite a chore, as you can imagine, and Claire began to look her age and she ceased to care. I hate to see a woman no longer fastidious in her appearance. I once knew a girl in college who neither bathed nor shaved her legs. By mid-terms, her grubby knees looked like the Castro brothers.[2]

But this doesn't explain what has happened since I set out to write my story. Three of the world's leading clerics tried to suppress this book. First, there was Rabbi Bris, the chaplain of the New York Athletic Club. Second, there were protests from the famous French evangelist, Billy Dimanche. Third, Cardinal Musial of St. Louis

[2] We all must share the same violent emotions about those fellows. I *hate* the Castro Brothers and refuse to buy their cough drops.

not only protested, he also lambasted me in his book *Bangles, Bobbles* and *Beads*.

Actually, this book is a sort of unprofound autobiography. It is my memoir. Any man who has led a full, interesting, or useful life can write a book. I'm a man who has *not* led a full, interesting, or useful life, so please give credit for trying to me, the Duke of Windsor, and the rest of us. Ever since the naked Eve asked of Adam, "How do you like dem apples?" folks have been trying to be profound. Wasn't it St. Christopher who said that when he traveled he never carried more than fifty dollars in cash? And Gaylord Housebreaker, who suddenly sat up in bed one morning and said, "Would you believe it? I have a cold." Others have attempted profundity in literature, as well as in oratory. Earl Long when he wrote *The Mature Mind*. Vance Studebaker in *The Waste Makers*. And so I've written *The Happy Sadist*, for this is a story that had to be told to a waiting and anxious world.

Not everyone will like it. Some will demur. But I suppose one must roll with the punches.

If the book doesn't succeed, there are other paths open to me. When you read further, you'll discover that mine has been a checkered and variegated career. Whatever the outcome, I can always get up off the floor and try again. It is useful in constructing a personal philosophy to remember the old adage about the tomcat who didn't quite clear the barbed-wire fence, and became a consultant.

—R.N.P.

THE HAPPY SADIST

CHAPTER 1

My name is Boswell Spavins. My happy life, like many others, began years and years ago.

I still have fond recollections of my mother taking me gently by the hand and leading me into the Ladies' Room. This is, of course, quite normal; all mothers take their little boys into Ladies' Rooms. But there were lingering effects. My mother took me to the Ladies' Room until I was fourteen.

Oh, at first it was fun, I suppose—drying myself under the warm-air blower while Mother, a dynamic woman, occasionally scribbled vitriolic rebuttals to the poetry on the wall. But as the years sped by, I grew so tall that I could look over the doors easily. Mother decided that I was big enough to try the Men's Room alone. It worked. But Mother always waited just outside the door and shouted needless instructions.

"Don't talk to anyone in there," she'd warn. "Men's Rooms are always full of degenerates."

She was right, as always. Mothers seem to know everything somehow and it makes one stop to wonder how they became so well informed. I've been in a heap of Men's Rooms since and, by George, there's been a degenerate in every one of them. Well, as my father said, getting to know a degenerate or two is all part of growing up.

Growing up was fun, and the two kids next door, John and Marsha, thought of really dandy games to play up in our old tree house. After John was sent away to the House of Correction, there was just Marsha and me and the old tree house. Maturing in that very American environment was a priceless experience.

Another part of growing up was the people. I remember them all so well, the big people and the little, who made up my home town of Weedville. We weren't very worldly, I suppose, but we enjoyed ourselves. The most popular man with us kids was a lovable fellow by the name of Mr. Hitler. He had a thick guttural accent and a funny little mustache. He'd fix our tricycles, blow up our balloons, or help us build fancy birdhouses. He even wallpapered the inside. Mr. Hitler could do just about anything he set his mind to. His motto was "There's no such word as KANT."

In 1936, the year F.D.R. defeated Alfred E. Neuman, Mr. Hitler left town and went back to Germany. He didn't return to Weedville until the summer of 1945. All of us had grown up by then, but we went down to the depot to welcome him home. We asked what he'd been up to in Germany all those years. (Our home-town paper carried only local news, as many small-town papers do.)

When he told us, it certainly was hard to believe. But I suppose like all of us, he had his faults. He was still the nicest man in my home town, and we were all pleased when he gave up wallpapering to become a successful entertainer. His comical undertaker act (he

would take a volunteer from the audience and embalm
him) did very well this past summer at a hotel in the
Catskills.

Another person I remember with fondness was my
first grade teacher, the portly old soul who first discovered that I had literary promise. She once gave us an
English assignment, to write about our lives as if we
were boys or a girl of a foreign land. A five-dollar
prize was to be awarded for the best paper.

My story was as follows:

Mama Was a Cannibal
BY BOSWELL SPAVINS

I will always remember Africa—the steaming jungles crawl-
ing with insects, the muddy rivers literally alive with alligator
and suède. I remember the witch doctor, the elephants, and
the colorful tribal dances. But most of all, when I think of
Africa, I remember Mau Mau.

I remember how she used to tuck me into bed at night, and
then pick up my little foot and say, "This little pygmy went
to market, this little pygmy stayed home," etc. etc. And then
she'd slip some poor Belgian's skull (a gift from the NAACP)
under my pillow—and sure enough, in the morning, there
would be a penny.

How the missionaries used to love to come to our village,
and never leave. Sometimes on a warm summer evening around
suppertime, I can still close my eyes and hear their screams,
the sweet sounds of home. Oh, how Mau Mau loved a good
missionary! She always made sure the table was set just so.
White wine with Catholics and red wine with Lutherans.
What a wonderful cook she was. I can still taste her Mashed
Methodist to this day. Her Eggplant Episcopalian, her Baptist

Brochette, her Pickled Presbyterian took the blue ribbon every year at the County Fair. And when it came to biscuits, you couldn't beat her Parkerhouse Holy Rollers.

Whenever I couldn't eat my dinner, Mau Mau would ask, "Don't you like missionary?"

"Yes," I'd burp, "but missionary doesn't like me." Yet that was seldom enough. Most of the time we all ate like savages.

The year I came home from the Antioch Business School, things just weren't the same. Mau Mau and Pau Pau had changed, grown older. Especially Mau Mau. She was critical of everyone, even of Dr. Schweitzer, who used to come over and play dinner music on the organ.

"Cool tune, Al," she'd say, "but it ain't danceable."[1]

One evening, though, Mau Mau did perk up a bit; it was good to see her be her old self again. We were having a rather important Englishman for dinner, and the meal was absolutely delicious. "Winston tastes good," said Mau Mau, licking her chops, "like an Englishman should."

Still, she was restless. She began to pace the floor at night, muttering, "Those drums! Those drums! Don't they ever stop beating?"

Mau Mau grew sullen, and she would often stand on her lip and pout. Gone were the days when Mau Mau would smile with those great lips. Gone were the golden moments when she would tiptoe up to my room late at night, and with those very lips slip a kiss under the door. Never again, I feared, would she joyously demonstrate the great versatility of those lips, showing off and sealing envelopes *after* she had dropped them into a mail box.

Mau Mau had changed. She had become belligerent, constantly argumentative. I remember the night she lost her temper and got into an altercation with Faubus, our chief. She really

[1] *Music to Eat Clerics By*—Schweitzer on RCA Victor, LP Album $3.98.

told him off but good, finally topping it off by hitting Faubus on the ear with her sneaker.

I remember Mau Mau. I remember how she looked when they brought her home that night. Bless her little shrunken head.

Needless to say, I won the five-dollar prize.

Want to know what I did with the five? I bought another dog. My new dog's name was Drambuie and we had endlessly amusing times together until, at last, one evening, he was run over by a truck. The truck driver, a Mr. Hoffa, was kindness itself and ran to call the vet. His sensitive, patrician face was twisted with remorse. He returned in ten minutes, dragging the vet by the ankle.

Dr. Spock operated immediately but poor Drambuie died, rather appropriately I thought, just after dinner. Mr. Hoffa and I took Drambuie's death well enough, but poor Dr. Spock was in tears. He said then and there that he was going to leave his veterinary practice to become a writer. Though it's difficult to believe, this came true. Years later, we learned he had written a book on how to raise children, in collaboration with Bing Crosby.

CHAPTER 2

When I think back, my first real girl friend was a natural beauty. Oh, there were other girls, to be sure, not all of them favored. But when the subject turns to first love, it can only bring to my mind the lovely drum majorette of Weedville High. She wore sweaters as if she invented them. I was no more impressionable than most, but moments after we met, I was smitten hopelessly with Cashmere Holstein.

When I took a first real look at Cashmere, she was coming out of algebra class. Her sweater came first. I could see that beneath that tranquil exterior was a full-blooded woman of pounding arteries and hot flowing juices. Her eyes, if I were to describe them in literary terms, were twin Walden Ponds of surface serenity, below which one could gaze into depths of undercurrents and rip tides. I ached for her, and the hurt mounted inside me and swelled up like a wild thing. But I was a shy, laconic farm boy so I did nothing for months except take incessant cold showers.

Along about February, the water became so cold that the showers were unbearable. What I needed was fast fast fast relief. (As you can tell, I was destined from the first for advertising.) And thus it happened that on a

Tuesday morning, right after biology, I forced my tall, gangling frame in the direction of Cashmere, quivering at every ganglion. I asked Cashmere if she would accompany me to the class sleigh ride on Friday night. Her white cardigan pressed close to me and I looked down reverently. Her Walden Pond eyes became twin maelstroms of fire and ice, and her breath came in short little gasps, as she realized that I was staring. At last her eyes once more became limpid pools and she said softly, almost in supplication, "Yes, I'd like to." It was a quiet beginning, but there was reason to believe she'd warm to me.

With her velvet hand in mine, we strolled to our next class. It was American history. The history teacher was George Valleyforge, perhaps the favorite teacher of Weedville High. Mr. Valleyforge announced to the class that today's lesson would deal with the young Washington. A mighty and patriotic roar went up from the class, as we were very fond of George Washington, there being no school on his birthday, February twelfth. Whipping out our musical instruments, we blasted a stirring rendition of the *Washington Post March* by Dr. John Phillip Seuss. The parade up and down the aisles was naturally led by Cashmere, who twirled her silver baton impressively at arm's length, for obvious reasons. After the demonstration for Washington we quietly resumed our seats and waited for Mr. Valleyforge to finish sweeping up the confetti and streamers. He began the lecture.

"Well," said the gentle pedagogue, "it seems there was this here cherry tree that young George cut down, and it fell up against Mount Vernon and smashed into the winders and like that. Old man Washington come out the house with a whip and asked little George, who was standing there holding an axe, who done it. As several witnesses had already signed affidavits, little George figured he was the fox in the hen house with feathers on his mouth, so what did he have to lose if he played it big?

"I cannot tell a lie," he said. "I done it!"

At this point in the lecture several of us broke down with emotion, put our heads on our desks, and sobbed without shame. Mr. Valleyforge ran up and down the aisles, passing out Kleenex, as he continued. He gave a beautiful display of his impromptu speaking style.

"Truth is always rewarded. A lie is an evil unto itself, and commits a disservice not to the listener but to the teller. Truth is a beacon that lights our way through a darkened world. It is a shining sword against falsity and ignorance. Above all, to thine own self be true, and thou canst not then be false to any man."

Stealing a look at Cashmere, I could see she was torn with honest emotion, her bosom heaving wildly as her breath came in short little gasps. I prayed the wool fiber would not take the tension, but it held.

After recess I walked home with Cashmere, carrying her books and baton. She was pensive and distant and my words to her of love were answered only by her phrases of raptured admiration for Washington and Truth.

Friday night came, after an eternity, and I prepared for the sleigh ride, anxious to be rolling in the hay with Cashmere Holstein in my arms. I was dressed warmly, but functionally. The mittens I wore could be pulled off in a jiff.

We all met at the livery stable. Soon we were jingling through the snowy night, laughing and singing to the rhythmic hoofbeats. Cashmere and I managed to bury ourselves down deep in the warm hay and unite our lips in warm, passionate kisses. As our temperatures rose, I suggested we both remove our overcoats. It was then, just as I anxiously took off my mittens, that I got the shock of my life.

Cashmere was as flat as a board!

"Where are they?" I whispered to Cashmere, feeling as though my heart would break in twain.

"Home in my dresser," she said, and her voice broke. "I've been living a lie. To mine own self I have not been true, but false. Do you hear, *false!* Every time you looked at me I was afraid you already knew, and that's what made me pant. George Washington made me face the facts. From now on Truth will be my beacon, lighting my way through a darkened world."

In a fit of blinding disappointment I jumped from the sleigh, intending to run home. I sailed through the air waiting to land in the soft snow. It was a long wait, for at that moment the sleigh was going over Devil's Gorge bridge.

Cashmere came to the hospital every day for weeks and lovingly autographed all seven of my casts. Concluding, I suppose, that Truth can sometimes be far more cruel than even double deception, her sweater once more took on its former contours and the wool fibers groaned under the strain like wharf ropes.

Nearly a month later I sat up in bed. My nurse ushered in a smiling visitor.

"Surprise!" Cashmere said, "my exercises paid off. Now they *are* real."

My blood pressure just couldn't take it. My head swam and I sank into a coma. They sent for the doctor.

"Do you think he'll live?" Cashmere asked.

"Perhaps," said the doctor cheerfully, "but tell him not to start reading any continued stories. Still, who knows? Maybe I can pull him through."

"Oh, Doctor," Cashmere panted, running forward to embrace him in gratitude. "You're wonderful. How can I ever repay you?"

"That's easy," said the doctor, ripping off his mittens. I struck at him with my casts.

The next day Cashmere came to visit as per usual, and perched on the edge of the bed.

"Boswell," she said, "there's another sleigh ride coming up Friday night. That's tomorrow. Think you can make it? This time you won't want to jump off and run home."

I groaned. Just as she was leaving she inhaled deeply going out the door and blew me a kiss.

"Get well soon," Cashmere suggested, "and you won't be sorry."

The next day there were reporters from the wire services and from the *Journal of the American Medical Association*. It was the first time, they observed, that any hospital had treated a patient with compound fractures and multiple internal injuries who had healed overnight.

CHAPTER 3

Please don't get the wrong idea from that episode in history class that I was a frivolous and inattentive *bon vivant*. Nothing could be farther from the truth.

Shortly after we studied George Washington, we moved on to the next event in American history, the Civil War. We found out some years later that the Civil War did not immediately follow George Washington. But a number of pages had been torn out of Mr. Valleyforge's history book by teen-age vandals, an act of violence that completely escaped his notice.

In our academic pursuit of the War between the States, Mr. Valleyforge left no stonewall unturned in his graphic efforts to act out the high lights of the war, from Antietam and Bull Run to Shiloh and Vicksvapor. Twin armies of inkwells, paper clips, and erasers moved strategically across the battlefield of his desk top. Time and again he would appear in class clad magnificently in a uniform of blue or gray, and would impart tirelessly to our hungry minds the conduct in battle of the great generals like Grant, Sheridan, Catton, McClellan, and Whitewall Jackson. We became devotees of that conflict.

In my opinion, the greatest of all Civil War personalities was an individual little known for his military ex-

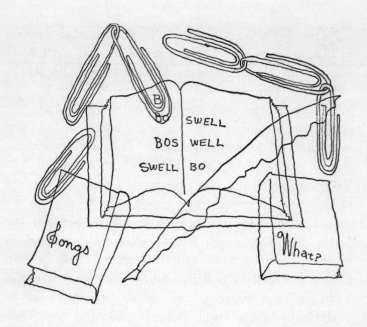

ploits. He was a man by the name of Robert E. Lee and although his name does not appear in any Southern folklore or records, I chose him as the subject for further study. The only fact I could dig up, unhappily, was that he rode a stallion named Fellow Traveler, a white horse to signal the spectators that Lee was one of the good guys.

Well, here's the history report on this Lee fellow. I guess it's unnecessary to tell you that it won the History Prize, which should prove to you that I was an able writer even in high school. I just wish all the editors who have rejected my manuscripts since could have read it.

Man in a Gray Flannel Suit

BY BOSWELL SPAVINS

This is a story of an obscure Civil War patriot, Robert E. Lee, and has no connection with the novel of the same name by Sloan Simpson.

In 1865 the Civil War was over. Cornwallis had surrendered at Yorktown and Raymond Massey had given his Gettysburg address. An obscure Confederate soldier, Bobby-Eddy Lee, stood in that Gettysburg crowd while President Massey mumbled a few words scrawled on the back of a parking ticket. The young Lee then headed home to "Cottonmouth," the old plantation.

His folks were powerful glad to see him coming up the road again, free of care, lightly leaping over the dead dogs. You can bet supper that night was some occasion. They had his favorite dish, a big, steaming bowl of weevils with plenty of grits.

THE HAPPY SADIST

After supper when Mother Lee had done the dishes and Daddy Lee had reburied the silver, Bobby-Eddy got all slicked up in his store clothes and put pomade on his hair. His childhood sweetheart, Scarlett O'Fever, lived nearby on the next plantation—the gracious, stately "Apartheid."

"It's Saturday night," chuckled jolly old Daddy Lee, "and I bet you're a fixin' to take her to town for the lynchin'!" He laughed once more. "Don't forget the double-header on Sunday."

"We'll be going to town all right," laughed our hero. "It's been four years!"

Time passed. Scarlett, as so many American kids do, got "in trouble," so she and Bobby were wed. The best man, curiously enough, was another military hero, George Custer, later killed at his last stand by the Sioux. At the time of his death, Custer had fifteen children and one on the way. History proudly bestowed on him the name of the river on whose banks he died: "The Little Big Horn."

For a while Bobby-Eddy and Scarlett did fairly well financially. Scarlett gave drawling lessons to the daughters of some of the rich carpetbaggers. Bobby-Eddy picked up a few bucks teaching pistol marksmanship to a youngster who lived nearby, a John Wilkes Booth. This was what was known in the South at that time as the Reinstruction Period.

But prosperity could not last forever, and in 1924 the pellagra crop failed. Scarlett was forced to take in washing.

One morning she was singing as she bent over the tub and, in a rare, gay, carnival mood, decided to play a joke on Lee. Pulling a sheet over her head, she sneaked up behind him and said, for lack of a better word, "Boo!" Scarlett's simple act started quite a fad, and many of their neighbors took it up until literally everyone joined in. Today in the South you may see this charming old custom still practiced, and you can bet that under each and every sheet there's a body that ought to be home washing somebody else's laundry.

Years passed, and Bobby-Eddy became a white-haired old man. He was Marse Robert now to all the blacks on "Cottonmouth," whom he referred to as his "cotton-pickin' hands."

And so, as it must to all men, the time came for ol' Marse Robert to cross the River Jordan. He closed his weary eyes and went through the Pearly Gates. But just as he died, he gave us one hint as to what Heaven would be like.

"Thank the Lord," he whispered. "Separate lunch counters."

On the night of graduation, I was introduced, jumped lightly as a roe to the lectern, cleared my rich baritone voice, and plunged:

"My topic this evening, as you can see on your programs if you'll only stop fanning for a moment—is 'Turning the Tables on Fate.'"

The fanning nervously abated.

"As we young people sit up here on the stage of this tradition-steeped institution, scratching in our caps and gowns, we know that we must now leave the arms of what in the Latin is called Mother, and go out into the cold cold world."

A few mothers took out their hankies.

"Our success will hinge on our youthful resilience, on being able to turn the least liability into a genuine asset. This is currently exemplified by one of our most popular classmates, and winner of the Literary Prize, Miss Betsy Ballpoint."

There was scattered applause.

"Recently, Miss Ballpoint was attacked and ravaged six times in an alley on the same day by the same man. Shortly thereafter, she sent her story in to the *Reader's*

Digest where it appeared as *The Most Unforgettable Character I've Ever Met*."[1]

The audience clapped and Miss Ballpoint smiled painfully.

"Here is still another instance. Remember when Clod's Corners stole our new cheer?"

At this point I was pelted good-naturedly with stones and garbage by both my classmates and the audience, for Clod's Corners was a nearby town, our bitterest rival; the very mention was enough to set them off.

"Did we give up after they took it? No! We immediately wrote another."

Whipping out a large white megaphone, with a big red W on it, I led the group in the cheer, to illustrate:

> *Two bits, four bits*
> *Six bits, a buck*
> *All for Weedville*
> *Stand up and holler!*

Everyone present, except a few poor cousins from Clod's Corners, jumped to his feet and the roar for dear old Weedville was deafening. When they had settled, I went on.

"Yes, we of Weedville may be proud. Proud of those who have graduated before us, for Weedville has indeed produced some greats.

"First, there was Hal Houndstooth, who invented the first dog food guaranteed to taste like a postman.

"In the field of Humanities, let us not overlook Alfred

---

[1] Her attacker was later apprehended by the police when he appeared as a guest on *What's My Line?*

E. Neuman, who founded the Neuman Club in colleges all over America.

"The music world has acclaimed Weedville's own Elvis Welk, who wrote such teenage hits as *Backseat Baby, Lord's Prayer Mambo, Drag Strip Sweetheart, Prissy Parents Polka, There'll be Blood on My Bumper, Overdue Blues,* and *Take Me, Sidney, I'm the Anxious Type.*"

At this point, several members of the Senior Class broke down and wept without shame. Certainly the recollection of an old sweet song has rung a tear from the most stoic of us all. Looking over my shoulder, I could see the last of the tears were wiped away, and the Seniors once more were passing the bottle around to further the festive spirit of the evening. I continued.

"Some great statesmen have been educated here at Weedville High. Let's not forget the man who came here as a foreign exchange student from Arizona, that great exponent of conservation and defender of the American way of life, Senator Berry Coldwater."

At the mention of Senator Coldwater's name, the audience went wild, and some even threw their hats into the air. The Weedville Silver Cornet Marching Band, sitting in the orchestra pit, struck up a thunderous *Stars and Stripes Forever.* Two veterans of World War I came forward, wearing Sam Browne belts and wraparound leggings, and presented me with the American Legion Medal. When I refused, saying that I had done nothing to deserve it, the audience pelted me again with stones and garbage, in a stirring display of patriotism. But I pressed on.

"Weedville has produced outstanding members of the

31

Dramatic Arts. Our Norma Vincent Peel, the sweetheart of American Burlesque, for one.

"In the field of sports, many big names once wore the uniform of the Weedville Lepers. As you know, the original name was Leopards, but there was that difficulty—the cross-eyed seamstress who made the uniforms couldn't spell."

There were titters out in the sea of faces.

"Don't forget Tripod Tyler, who was 18 feet tall. Only first baseman in the league who could touch three bases at once."

I could have gone on forever, but it seemed pointless, as most of the audience had gone. Also, the Seniors were anxious for their diplomas, and the Faculty even more impatient to draw their final checks so they could take off for vacation.

Many teachers had jobs for the summer, as dish-washers, bus boys, on construction crews, and in coal mines. It gives teachers the opportunity to widen their scope of experiences, and many returned to write short essays in the fall, usually called *How I Spent My Summer Vacation*. Usually a summer job for a teacher is just a lark, but it does round out his personality, and triples his yearly income.

"In conclusion . . .

At this point those remaining applauded with such appreciation that I bowed and rejoined my classmates. An orator knows when to quit.

CHAPTER 4

To understand how a poor but honest boy like myself gets a higher education, you have to look for the people behind him. I have two aunts, and both their names are Lola. One married well, a rich doctor Getz. The other was in love briefly with a ne'er-do-well, a man called Frank Wantz, who left her shortly after the nuptials. But these two women, Lola Wantz, and her sister, Lola Getz, were of incalculable help to me. Lola Getz, my rich aunt, has a swimming pool shaped like a kidney. Lola Wantz, my poor aunt, had a kidney shaped like a swimming pool, which she sold to a Miami Beach hotel, making attendance at Coolidge College possible for me.

College was a great experience. I feel certain that without it I would not be the charming, polished, and poised person I am today. College means academics and sports, to be sure. But it also affords the student a cultural and social broadening that cannot be duplicated elsewhere. If I had to summarize what a college education meant to me, the answer could only be centered about my closest associate, and perhaps the warmest relationship of my life. He was idol, muse, teacher, and friend. He was my roommate, Rabbit McSperm.

Normal in nearly every other respect, Rabbit had one

paramount eccentricity. His capacity for the companionship of women was nothing short of olympic. He was a physical phenomenon, an amateur Johns Manville without portfolio.*

But Rabbit had his cross to bear, for unless he made love to a girl at least twice a day, he would break out all over in hives. Every evening he headed straight for the girls' dormitory, and, after making his nocturnal devotions, he would return smiling and hiveless. His parents were on campus for Homecoming Weekend. They were perfectly normal. I had quite a good visit with them one evening. They were much interested in our welfare and both were delightfully informed people. During most of the conversation Mr. McSperm was grappling on the floor with a leggy coed. Mrs. McSperm was equally companionable, running her hand up under my shirt and urging me to call her by her first name, Amber. They were just plain folks, average in every respect.

Rabbit and I were holding a small celebration one evening (Blue Cross had just granted him premarital maternity coverage) when he looked at his watch and announced that he must be off for the girls' dorm.

"Let me go with you, Rabbit," I asked, my deep gray eyes pleading far more than my words.

"No, Boswell, you'd only get in the way."

"Please, please," I begged, stamping my foot. "You won't hear a peep out of me. I'll just watch."

"Well, okay," Rabbit consented. "But why stop there? Illisa's roommate is always available; we'll make it a foursome. But *we* get the back seat."

* No relation to Portfolio Rubirosa

"Fine," I squealed with delight. "I'll jump in the shower and be ready in a jiff."

"Not *now*, Stupid. You shower afterward, not before!"

We borrowed a car from Avis Hertz, a girl who sat next to me in economics, and roared off to our fate. The tires squealed their protest as we rounded the curve near the bust of Alger Hiss, the founder of the college. Rabbit suggested throttling down after I had, like a child in wild anticipation, taken a short cut through the Administration Building.

Pulling up at the girls' dorm, we beeped the horn, and two shapely coeds came slowly grinding down the walk to meet us. Rabbit did the honors.

"Illisa Illicit and Ova Sexton, may I present my roommate, Boswell Spavins. Bos, you get Ova. Illisa and I get the back seat."

They jumped in the car, I gunned the motor in a brilliant touch of suggestiveness, and we were off.

"Can't we go to the movies?" suggested Illisa. "At the Bijou there's Tab Collar and Lava LaTramp in *You're Breaking My Glasses*."

After we had driven several miles, I suddenly asked where we were headed.

"To Statuatory Park," came the muffled instruction from Rabbit, from his vantage point under a blanket in the back seat."

"Goody," cried Ova, "I took ceramics last semester and I'm bats over statues."

"I'm pigeons over statues," I said, and we all giggled at my quick wit until we arrived at the Park. Rabbit suggested that Ova and I take a walk despite the fact it was now raining quite hard.

"Not on your life, Rabbit," I protested. "You said I could watch."

"Say," said Illisa, "at the Rialto is Tonto and Gina Garlic in *Back in the Saddle Again*."

Ova tried to make conversation and said dryly, "Rabbit tells us you're from Weirdsville."

"That's funny," I puzzled. "He knows very well I'm from Weedville."

"Why don't you and Ova take a stroll in the rain," suggested Rabbit. "It's romantic."

"I wish we'd gone to the movies," mumbled Illisa. "I'm dying to see Rod Eveready as Chief Thundermug in *Standing Up in a Canoe*."

"You could stand under a tree," Rabbit insisted.

"If you think I'm getting my hair soaked to cool you off, you're crazy," Ova declared.

"Yep," I reflected, "we've been living in Weedville since 1935."

"A little rain makes people cling together," said Rabbit poetically.

"Could we stop at the drive-in movie on the way back?" implored Illisa.

"Yes," agreed Ova, "one with a john."

"Shucks," Rabbit said, giving me a friendly slap on the back, "a little rain water never hurt anyone."

"Before Weedville, we lived in Clod's Corners."

"Why didn't I go before leaving the house?" Ova said.

"Last week I saw Everett Dirkson in *Somewhere Right of Center*. Boy, is he neat," Illisa drooled.

"A big boy like you afraid of a little rain," kidded Rabbit, but his slap this time was somewhat harder, more like a shove.

"We like Weedville better than Clod's Corners."

"The rain on the roof is driving me nuts," Ova lamented.

"Nebby Reynolds, the Hollywood gossip columnist, said that Dirk's a cinch to win the Academy Award for that picture," said Illisa.

"Let me open the door for you," offered Rabbit, putting his foot in the middle of my back.

"Though Clod's Corners had a better public library."

"He can really act," said Illisa.

"Someday cars will have johns," grumbled Ova, doubled over.

"C'mon, Boswell," pleaded Rabbit, "I'm starting to itch."

"But the scenery around Weedville is far superior."

"—and sing and dance, too," Illisa added.

"I can't stand it any longer," panted Rabbit.

"Jesus, will you hurry up so we can go home," Ova said.

"Why you miserable broad," screamed Illisa at her roomy, "I suppose you're a saint. What about you and Stan Studfee at the Sophomore Hop? In the *orchestra* pit no less."

"You should talk, you round-heeled tramp," Ova parried neatly. "What about you and Andy Anxious in the trunk of his MG?"

"Oh yeah? Well, listen, Miss Bitch, it's all over campus about you and George Grab on the Delta Chi fire escape," laughed Illisa, "—hanging by your heels."

"What about you and . . ."

The trip homeward that evening was clouded with gloom and hardly anyone spoke. Occasionally Illisa would suggest we stop at a drive-in movie with no rest room. Periodically Ova would push for a rest room that did not feature movies. Other than that it was a dull, dreary ride.

Rabbit stayed in the car and scratched, but I walked the girls to their door and presented each of them with a colorful folder prepared by the Weedville Travel Bureau. Both Illisa and Ova expressed their appreciation with adjectives I'd never heard before.

English majors, I mused.

Later that evening Rabbit and I relaxed back in our room. I opened a bottle of Coke and Rabbit opened a bottle of calamine lotion to smear on his already blotchy chest. We discussed my social shortcomings until far into the night. After that, Rabbit went to sleep and I began the arduous task of undoing the knots he had tied in my clothes.

A week later the unhappy double-date with Rabbit, Ova and Illisa had faded into the dim past, and I was again my usual optimistic self. In fact, I was so optimistic that I decided to ask the best-looking girl on campus for a date.

When Ecstacy Proneville swished her heavenly bottom along the quad, there wasn't a male within a quarter of a mile whose head did not turn, whose eyes did not bulge, and whose imagination did not soar. From the front, her face would have made Helen of Troy look like Mrs. Khrushchev. From the rear, her tight skirt gave the illusion of two melons fighting in a burlap bag. But as with any great beauty, there is always great sadness. Ecstacy would have nothing to do whatsoever with any of the boys on campus. Her only interest was in reading.

The big event of the year was coming up, the Costume Ball, and I decided to invite Ecstacy, futile though it might be. Anyone else would have sidled up to her and popped the invite. But not me, for I was shrewder far. Racing down to the Acne Costume Rental Company, I rented a Santa Claus suit from Mr. Acne himself. Dressed as Santa I ran back to campus despite the fact it was a hot afternoon in May, sought out Ecstacy, and invited her. I suggested that she could go as a reindeer.

"Beat it, Creep," she said kindly, and returned to her book. She was reading *Ivanhoe*.

I don't give up easily, so I tore back to gain the counsel of Mr. Acne. We exchanged the Santa outfit for a rabbit suit, and I merrily hopped back to campus, sought out Ecstacy, and suggested she go as Elwood P. Dowd.

"Get lost," she said, and continued reading *The Crusades*.

Back to Mr. Acne I hopped and hopefully tried several more costumes, but all in vain. He had a splendid inventory, yet I was equally unsuccessful as Sister Kenny, Vic Tanny, Margaret Sanger, Beatrice Fairfax, George Lincoln Rockwell, Helen Keller, Gunga Din, Lassie, and Dave Beck.

Even Mr. Acne said I was quite fetching as Bathsheba, but Ecstacy still ignored me. She never even looked up from her book, *Knights of the Round Table*. What was I to do? O Lost! Mr. Acne listened sympathetically to the whole story and suggested I get a good night's sleep.

Several hours later, I awoke with a start and raced

down to the Acne Costume Rental Company. Mr. Acne slept over the store. When I woke him, he sat up in bed blinking.

"Knights!" I yelled, grabbing him by the lapels of his prisoner pajamas. "She's crazy about knights!"

Mr. Acne said he was too and went back to sleep.

At last it arrived: the evening of the Costume Ball. I was busy up in my room getting into my suit of armor. Naturally Ecstacy had agreed to accompany me when I hinted I would go as the famed Mormon knight, Brian Debois Gilbert. Happy as a lark and whistling a few bars of *Greensleeves*, I tightened the last of the nuts and bolts and went clanking off to the sorority where I rang the Gamma Ray's doorbell. I chuckled at my own cleverness.

The housemother answered. I bowed low in knightly gesture. Mother Gabor announced me, and Ecstacy oozed down the stairs as Lady Rowena. She stared. Then she told me I'd make a terrific knight.

"You'd make a terrific night yourself," I quipped, and we all chuckled over my priceless bon mot adapted from Mr. Acne's churlish remark, especially Mother Gabor.

At the Ball, Ecstacy snuggled warmly in my arms and danced as close to me as the suit of armor would permit. After a time the metal got so hot you couldn't touch it, so I suggested we stroll in the moonlight down by the lake. We walked way out to the end of the pier and stretched out on big gray planks. Without hesitation, I took this loveliest of all creatures into my arms, and she was melons, melons, melons!

"Behold," I said, whispering a well-chosen line from *Ivanhoe* into her waxen ear, "the fair Rowena."

Her response was overwhelming.

"Make love to me, Sir Knight," she gasped. "Take me, for I am thine."

This was the moment of moments, the chance of chances, the golden gate that opens but once in a life-time. Opportunity wasn't just knocking gently; it was smashing the door in with a battering ram. This was it, Paradise was at my feet. I'd better not blow it. With trembling fingers I took the necessary steps for the next move. I fumbled for the wrench that I had, with great foresight, stuffed down inside my gauntlet. Feverish with excitement, I at first could not locate the wrench. If it was mislaid, then so was I. But with a grateful sigh I located it. I started to loosen the first nut. It seemed like an eternity, but slowly and surely it came loose and I put down the wrench to finish extracting the bolt with my hand.

"Hurry, darling," said Ecstacy, writhing. "Hurry!"

Then it happened. I reached for the wrench again and, by mistake, dropped it between the huge planks on the pier. There was a short silence, followed by the awful moment of truth.

Splash.

Both Ecstacy and I were hit with the stark realization. There is nothing as hopeless as the feeling that a chap gets when he is about to make love to the most gorgeous girl on campus, is locked inside a suit of armor, and drops the wrench off a pier into deep water. Everyone who has experienced this feeling knows what real tragedy is.

"How could you?" Ecstacy screamed, and sitting up she gave me a stinging slap across the visor.

"Don't worry," I said, "I'll dive for it."

My brave words fell on deaf ears. Ecstacy jumped to her feet, straightened her clothing, and marched off, leaving me alone with the bitter disappointment seething within. The hot tears that I could hold back no longer fell from my deep brown eyes and left little rust spots on my gleaming breastplate. I walked dejected toward the edge of the pier, knowing that now there was only one course left open. For this noble knight, there was but one way out.

Just as I was about to jump, a thought struck me. I couldn't throw myself into the lake and drown, because first I had to return the suit of armor to the costumer. Greatly relieved, I wheeled in my tracks, soaked my feet in the shallow part of the lake for a moment to cool off the hot metal, and went clanking sadly back to campus.

The next day I learned that Ecstacy had returned to the dance, but had left early with someone dressed handsomely as King Arthur. In description, he sounded strangely like Mr. Acne.

Well, years have passed since I took Ecstacy to the Costume Ball, and the memory has faded in the twilight. The whole incident has been blotted from my mind and left me unaffected quite. Except, to be sure, that whenever I hear the subtle sound of a zipper, I have to soak my feet instantly in cold water.

CHAPTER 5

Compared to institutions of higher learning such as Harvard and Yale and Rutgers, probably Coolidge College is not quite as well-known, except among the intelligentsia. But no one can ever say that Coolidge did not have a superior basketball record the year that I almost made the team.

Now without a doubt, the most important ingredient in a great team of any kind is a great coach. Ours was a man named Absorbine. His father, Abner Absorbine, had been a great Coolidge basketball coach in his day and had invented the forward pass. He had twelve children. The first eleven were girls named Agatha, Agnes, Alice, Audrey, Armina, Annabel, Akron, Amos, Andy, Aspirin, and Anacin. The twelfth was a boy and he was named Abner Absorbine, Jr., after his father. As young Abner was growing up, he lived in the aura of a good father, a decent coach, beloved by not only the student body of Coolidge but by the faculty and the alumni as well.

His father never had much time to spend with little Abner or his eleven sisters. Instead he spent most of his time down in his laboratory trying to invent the forward pass. Time and time again he would fail while his wife and eleven daughters chided, saying mean things like, "You'll never invent the forward pass." Even little Abner gave up hope. Yet his father was not to be disheartened and one evening he came up from his laboratory in the basement carrying a strange object. A chill froze in the son's veins.

"I've done it!" the older man cried with glee. "I've invented the forward pass and here it is for all to see."

Well, you can just imagine how his family crowded around and admired the forward pass that he had so skillfully invented. All, that is, except Abner, Jr. who realized that now his father would be not only a good but a famous coach which meant that he, little Abner, would grow up with a competitive father complex. In a blind fit of jealousy, young Abner snatched the forward pass from his father's hands and threw it out the window. This was a memorable moment in the world of sport, to be compared to the time when the plate umpire asked Babe Ruth a question and the immortal Babe pointed to the Men's Room in center field. Yes, it marked the very first completed forward pass; the ball was gathered in by a passer-by.

The invention of the forward pass made Absorbine, Sr., a hero practically overnight. His home became a center of interest, and reporters from all the important newspapers came to interview him and the family, to snap their pictures, posing with the forward pass. Little Abner's competitive father complex grew within him so that he could finally take it no longer. He ran away from home.

Soon, he teamed up with a beautiful young gypsy. The gypsy's name was Crystal Ballbearing and the happy young couple became quite solvent by reading palms and tea leaves and foretelling the future. Just as a sideline they published a magazine about palmistry, called *Fortune*. After it became enormously successful, Abner and Crystal decided that something was missing in their lives. They wanted more than just money; they wanted attainment. Besides, they were sick of each other. They went their separate ways. Crystal went to Russia and became a prima ballerina. Abner took a course in physical education by mail and almost immediately became the basketball coach at Coolidge College.

In fact, this was the same year that I almost made the team. As you know, Coolidge was a very small school. There were only six who tried out, therefore one of us had to be the substitute. But my name appeared on the program right along with the fellows who made the first team. The program read as follows:

COOLIDGE BASKETBALL TEAM

PLAYER	NO.	HEIGHT	WEIGHT	HOME TOWN
Merrill	1	5′2″	120	Westfield, New Jersey
Lynch	2	5′1″	119	Westover, Massachusetts
Pierce	3	5′½″	118	Weston, Connecticut
Fenner	4	4′11″	117	Westport, New York
Smith	5	4′10″	116	Westbrook, Pegler
Substitute				
Spavins	84	6′4″	190	Weedville, New York

As you can see I didn't quite make the team as a regular because of my height, not an inconsiderable handicap. A small school, the gym was even smaller. The ceiling, in fact, was just six feet from the floor. Basketball at Coolidge was for that reason a short man's game.

You are probably also wondering why my number was 84 instead of 6. Well, the explanation here is equally simple. When the treasurer of the college athletic department ordered the new basketball uniforms he forgot about the substitute and only ordered five. Therefore, I had to wear one of the old uniforms. The old uniforms were ordered in 1895. They were different in a few particulars. I wore a red satin cap, a long-sleeved, white jersey, red satin knickers and white shin guards. This was somewhat embarrassing as the school colors had long since been changed from red and white to blue and gold. My sneakers had the old-fashioned square toes which are nearly obsolete today due to the gradual disappearance of the drop kick. Still, what with one thing and another, I was reasonably easy to spot, perhaps because my number was 84, a simple number to remember.

Abner Absorbine, Jr. was not a great coach by any means. In fact he knew nothing whatever about basketball. But he did know, thanks to his marriage, how to foretell the future and in the locker room prior to every game he'd tell us exactly what the other team was planning to do. He would sit cross-legged on the floor of the locker room, a turban on his head, gazing into the flames of a bronze incense burner. Sooner or later, the spirits would make contact with him, and he drew on the floor in a quivering hand the plays of the opposing team. The spirits would point out the holes in the defense as well. It was uncanny but well within the NAAU rules, and it worked. We always won.

The game that I remember best was the last game of the season against our arch rival, Millard Filmore. Prior to the game we were in the locker room as usual, sitting on the floor in a circle, holding hands and murmuring the magic words, drinking the secret potions. A typical American collegiate basketball team (except that we had not been bribed) with ordinary pre-game jitters. Then Coach Absorbine noticed that Smith was missing.

What were we to do? When the phone rang, it was Smith. He had been badly beaten up by some roughneck, a coarse chap called Beane, and was in the hospital. Needless to say, Smith couldn't play. What were we to do? I held my breath, knowing that this was my big chance. At last I might actually get into a game instead of just being a substitute.

"What shall we do?" wailed the coach.

"There's only one thing we can do," said Merrill, the captain of the team, looking at me, "we've got to play against Filmore with only four men."

"Of course," said Absorbine, "why didn't I think of that? It's obvious."

They all agreed it was obvious. I heard a noise and knew it was my heart breaking.

It was quite a game. Millard Filmore had a tough, fast, and aggressive team. To make matters worse they had a rugged center by the name of Wheezer White who was 5′4″ and made our boys look like midgets. Wheezer was scoring most of the points for Millard Filmore. The crowd was filled with Wheezer's friends and relatives, most of them shanty Irish down from Boston to see the game. Whenever he would score a basket they would all yell, scream, and drink scotch.

At half time the score was 4 to 2 in favor of Filmore. The atmosphere in our locker room was one of silence and gloom. Abner Absorbine, Jr. paced back and forth, approaching nervous collapse. It was tragic to see this huge, hulking man in such condition. At last he spoke.

"Golly Moses," he said in the plaintive manner of coaches everywhere, "whatever are we going to do? If you don't win I'm going to hate you all. You know how much winning this Filmore game means to me."

We nodded. If Coolidge had an undefeated season, Coach Absorbine would get the head coaching job opening up at Yale. It was his one big chance.

The old clock on the wall said it was time to go back out on the court and warm up for the second half. We rose and, putting our arms around each other in a circle, gave our usual cheer:

> *"Walnut, almond,*
> *Filbert, pecan.*
> *Who can win it?*
> *We can. We can!"*

Inspired, we went racing from the locker room with light hearts. Our starting four took their places on the court, and I resumed my seat on the stool. (No sense in having a long bench for just one substitute, was there?)

The second half began. It was a grim, gruesome replica of the first. The precious seconds ticked by and the score mounted. With five minutes left to play and Millard Filmore leading 6 to 4, Wheezer White's asthma was beginning to bother him. But despite his allergy he was still all over the court—passing, shooting, fouling, double-dribbling.

At this point in the story I must mention one most important fact. It is a time-honored Coolidge College custom that, on the night of the last game of the season against Filmore, all coeds wear corsages of the Coolidge flower, ragweed. When Filmore called a time out, I saw what you might call my goldenrod opportunity. Snatching a corsage from a passing cheerleader, I tore it into tiny bits and joined the Filmore five on the floor. I mingled in their huddle so cleverly that they didn't even know I was there. So stealthy was I, that Wheezer White didn't even notice when I slipped the ragweed down the front of his shirt. Then I slyly stole back to the stool. No one had seen me or heard me. (They may be old-fashioned but you can't beat square-toed sneakers for everyday sneaking.)

The game resumed with only one minute to play. Wheezer White's terrible attack of asthma caused him to leave the game. Now Filmore had only four men, as in a bold display of confidence they did not bring any substitutes. This was Coach Absorbine's chance to outnumber them. He turned to me.

"Okay," he said, "you can play. Don't forget to report to the official."

"*Yahoo*," I yelled, and leaped to my feet. But in my excitement I jumped up too fast and rammed my head through the soundproof Armstrong ceiling. Despite my best efforts, there was no way to get loose. I remained there until the end of the game, unable to see, as I was in darkness from the nostrils up. When I finally extracted my head the game was over and by adroit use of the forward pass, Coolidge had beaten Millard Filmore 8 to 6.

My fellow teammates crowded around me; they knew what I had done to save the day. Hugging and congratulating me, they hoisted me to their shoulders, ramming my head through the ceiling once more. But I was drunk with victory and cared not a fig.

Years upon years have passed since those golden days at Coolidge. Recently, I went back for Homecoming Weekend and in a quiet moment walked through the hallowed halls of the athletic department. In the trophy room hangs a plaque commemorating that triumph over Filmore, 8 to 6. Nailed to the plaque is the first forward pass, invented by the father of our beloved coach.

As I turned to leave the trophy room a showcase blocked my passage, and a stab of emotion pierced my very soul when I suddenly saw its contents. It was my old uniform, number 84, that had been retired on the spot, never to be worn again by another athlete. Underneath the uniform was a little stool, to which a gold plaque had been attached and inscribed:

> "In memory of Boswell Spavins, the greatest substitute who ever wore a Coolidge uniform."

Well, you may call me a sentimental fool if you wish, but the floor at my feet became damp with tears.

CHAPTER 6

After reading of the episodes with Ecstacy and Rabbit and the early days on the team, you may think that my college career was just one disappointment after another. Nothing could be further from the truth. Again in college literary ability made me stand out among my fellow students. Although they still pelted me with stones and garbage on occasion, both the student body and the faculty were impressed by my swell command of the language.

The English prof in particular, was a great source of encouragement. Had it not been for his inspiring talks, there can be no doubt that I would not be the successful writer I am today.

"Spavins," he used to say, "this here paper is brilliant. Brilliant! You write gooder'most nearly every other kid in 'a place."

When the time came to write my English thesis, there was no trouble in thinking of a subject or an approach. I decided to do a research paper that would incorporate all of the various basic, essential facts that I had gleaned during my time in college. While other students used the library for digging out information, I shunned this practice as callow and immature. If one has to be constantly looking up data, it certainly does not indicate a grasp of one's subject. So, instead of using the reference library, I decided to call upon that great mother lode of information, my brain.

When writing a research paper, it is imperative to choose a subject that is not narrow. If you do, you might soon run out of things to say. In other words, the whole purpose is to be broad and not vertical. College, after all, is meant to broaden, to enlarge your range of interest, and generally widen your scope, whatever that means. So it would be folly to confine genius and a wealth of experiences to parochial discourse. The subjective horizons of one topic alone were as repugnant to me as a bath in warm beer, and I properly decided not to be limited, but rather to expand and expound at the same time.

The paper would incorporate not only my obvious literary talent but classroom subjects as well. It would touch on the arts, anthropology, science, and sociology. My fifth subject was taught by my English prof, of course, and, in deference to him, I decided to write the paper in English. My thesis follows. I feel confident that it will illustrate not only the horizontal reservoir of knowledge that one compiles in college nowadays, but also the student's capacity for correlating this vast storehouse of information into an impressive canal of orderly thought. It will attempt not only to manifest the performing art of the dance and its influence on the population explosion, but will also codify the extraneous relationship of American heritage and its direct effect on contemporary aeronautical sciences.

Well, now that your intellectual appetite has been whetted to razor sharpness, here is the thesis. One word of caution, however. Don't read it for itself alone. The things to look for are symbolism, alliteration, onomatopoeia, streptococcus, and also to ask yourself this question: What is the author really trying to say?

A Brief History of the Bunny Hop, the American Indian, the Evolution of Flight, and Planned Parenthood
BY BOSWELL SPAVINS

History tells us the first man to fly the Atlantic was Charles Lindbergh. Nothing could be farther from the truth. It was, in actuality, an American folk-hero, Paul Bunsen.

Old Elijah Bunsen, the father of our hero, brought his family over on the Mayflower in 1492 and settled in Salem, Massachusetts. The Bunsen family grew and grew (birth control information is banned in Massachusetts) and the thirty-fifth child was named Paul.

By this time, Elijah was up to here with his role as a Pilgrim father, and the Bunsens agreed on no more kids. Unfortunately, they were overheard and were burned at the stake as heretics[1] by the good people of Salem.

Paul, however, escaped the Bunsen burners. He ran away and was adopted by Indians. His foster parents, Tommy Hawk, with his wife Kitty, already had two sons, Wilbur and Orville, but they raised Paul as their own. He shared their hearth and home, being offered the same privileges as Wilbur and Orville, such as carving initials on their chests, sleeping in the rain, and eating raw snakes.

[1] For further information on religion in America, read Sinclair Lewis' commercial but interesting novel, *Elmer Valo*.

Many moons passed, and the time came for the three young braves to prove their manhood. This was done, as is common knowledge, by demonstrating that one could kill another Indian with a tomahawk. With typical Indian cunning the three boys selected and killed three old women of their village.

The last and final test was to be daubed with paint and feathers, climb the tallest pine, and jump. The three boys climbed to the top of a giant pine. Paul stared open-mouthed as Wilbur and Orville went splattering on the rocks below, and the whole Indian village commented sullenly on how tall the pines had grown since the initiation of the last year's pledge class.

From his lofty perch, Paul was still timid, but in the crowd below he spied the chief's lovely daughter, Hot Blanket, with whom he was engaged in a feckless affair. Pride bested judgment, so Paul shut his eyes and plunged forward.

"Your fly is open," Hot Blanket yelled as he dove out into the air.

"What?" he shouted.

"Fly!" Hot Blanket repeated.

The power of suggestion at times of stress is one of the epochal mysteries of the mind. Paul instinctively spread his feathery arms and neatly pulled out of the power dive, but the momentum carried him clear across the Atlantic Ocean where he landed safely in France.

The French people stared at him curiously, for at that time a half-naked man swooping down out of the air, smeared with paint and feathers, was a rare sight along the West Bank. The Art Students' Ball has since changed all that.

When Paul told them what he had done, they swarmed over him in profuse affection, smothering him with French hugs and French kisses. In his statement to the Paris press, *Au Gratin,* he described his historic flight in unforgettable words as "like a trip to the moon on gossamer wings."

He was nicknamed "Le Hop" by the fun-loving Parisites, and a new dance, the Bunsen Hop, was created in his honor. It was later renamed the Bunny Hop because of Paul's success with Frenchwomen. (When Lindbergh landed in France many years later, this dance was renamed the Lindy.)

Paul never returned to the Indian village of his boyhood. Hot Blanket was charming enough, but a girl who constantly reeks of moose meat exerts little appeal after one has seen Paris, so he stayed in France and lived happily ever after. The feathers on his arms had started to sprout, and so a new business was born. Paul made a good living growing feathers, selling them to labor leaders for their bedding.

Meanwhile, what became of his boyhood associates? Well, Hot Blanket changed her name and went away to college at Carlisle University. While a student there, she excelled at athletics and became famous under the name of Jim Thorpe. Wilbur and Orville recovered, went to Boston, and made a fortune banning birth-control information books and social security. They later opened up an office at Hiatusport.

So, as you can see, this certainly explodes the Lindbergh theory into a cocked hat. But it would of come out sooner or later.

Needless to say, after I had written this thesis there were offers from every school for almost every kind of scholarship, and from publications of all sorts for serial rights. But I spurned them all, turning instead westward toward New York, where I somehow sensed that there was a place for me.

CHAPTER 7

After graduating from college my first job was playing shortstop for a team in Sit In, Georgia. The name of the team was the Quadroons, later identified as the High-Yellow Sox, when they became part of another league. That was only summer employment.

My first *real* job was when I came to New York and gained a position as Assistant Mail Boy with a large Madison Avenue advertising agency, Pearl & Swine. Because of my college degree, the job paid thirty-five dollars a week. Two duties were specified: I was to wear suits from Abercrombie & Fitch and always lunch at the Stork Club. A & F suits, it turned out, were a little scratchy, but the food at the Stork was superb. I became a regular there. In fact, I got to know the proprietor, Sherman Adams, quite well.

My time in the Mail Room was occupied primarily with licking stamps, which served me well in experience for the later bootlicking I performed as an executive. I had only been in the Mail Room for six years, when Mr. Fatbracket's secretary phoned down that I was to report to him at once. As J. Pitchblende Fatbracket was a Senior Executive V.P. on the highly coveted Leaky account, needless to say I tucked in my shirt, checked my fly, and smoothed down my flaxen hair before racing up to knock timidly on his door.

Mr. Fatbracket looked up and then down at his shoes. "Never mind," he said, "I don't need one today."

After telling him who I was, he motioned me in and bade me sit in one of the large red leather club chairs. I sat, and Mr. Fatbracket waited politely for the seat cushion to stop hissing before he began.

"Spavins," he said, "I've had my eye on you for some time. I like the way you do your work. You stick with it, you have style. You're the only kid in the Mail Room who applied for the job with your resumé printed on scented stationary."

I smiled modestly, adding that I could also recite *If* by Rudyard Kiplinger.

"I like the way you eat lunch," he continued, "for I butter both sides of a slice of bread, too."

"There's two sides to everything," I agreed, awed at my own boldness.

"And," he continued, smiling, "although you probably should wear socks even if it is summer, you are a presentable dresser."

I stood up and turned around several times so Mr. Fatbracket could admire my scratchy suit. I sat down again. Mr. Fatbracket stopped drumming his fingers on the desk, and continued.

"Boswell, we at P & S think you'd make a good member of our first team. What do you say? Would you like to be a Jr. Account Executive on Leaky Septic-Tank?"

Leaping over the desk and throwing my arms around his neck, sobbing great, salty tears of gratitude, I covered Mr. Fatbracket with warm, wet kisses. For indeed, beyond that, I could not speak, and could only nod my head in silent acceptance.

Mr. Fatbracket took out his hanky and wiped my tear-stained cheeks, and then dabbed at his own glue-smeared cheeks (I had licked a goodly number of stamps that morning).

"Well, Spavins," he said, "report up here Monday morning and we'll meet the client."

Lester Leaky, it turned out, was a hairy hulk of two-hundred thirty pounds who had a handshake like the village blacksmith, which he accompanied by as warm a smile as any Cro-Magnon might render. Mr. Fatbracket introduced us, and then beat a hasty retreat to "another meeting."

Mr. Leaky studied me carefully. I fidgeted in my tweeds while Mr. Leaky sat there, quietly pulling the wings off a fly. At last he spoke. His voice was calm and deliberate; this was a man accustomed to command.

"Sonny, you are the fifteenth man assigned to this account in the last six months. You make good or I'll have you flushed down a narrow pipe."

I ran wide-eyed and screaming to the protective wing of Mr. Fatbracket, who turned out to be hiding under the sink in the executive bathroom.

"Has he gone?" asked Mr. Fatbracket, quivering.

My next meeting with Mr. Leaky was somewhat better. Perhaps because it was in his office. We had prepared several exciting new ads which I tucked under my arm, and I grabbed the train for Seepage, Connecticut—home of the Leaky Septic-Tank Corps.

The NY, Huntington & Hartford bucked and swayed

its way through Greenwich, Stamford, Darien, Westport and finally wheezed into the Seepage station in record time. It was four and a half hours late. I hopped a cab to the Leaky Septic-Tank Corps., and in no time was in Mr. Leaky's office, displaying the latest creative efforts of Pearl & Swine.

Ad No. 1 was a glamorous shot of lovely Zsa Zsa Garbo standing beside a picture of the product. The copy said: Zsa Zsa admits that the secret of her popularity is her Leaky Septic-Tank. This of course was followed by the client's traditional slogan, "Don't Be Reeky, Buy a Leaky."

Ad No. 2 showed Gregory Peck, Rock Hudson, Tab Hunter, and Sol Mineo standing around admiring Zsa Zsa's Leaky Septic-Tank and remarking on how beautifully it fitted into the decor.

Ad No. 3 showed Zsa Zsa and her mother and sisters all comparing their Leaky Tanks as to color, shape, use, and capacity. The copy line throughout was: "The Septic-Tank of the Stars."

"Great campaign!" thundered a pleased Mr. Leaky, giving me a slap on the back hearty enough to break the neck of a buffalo, "but it still needs something. It lacks a spiritual quality, somehow, and also needs more corporate identification."

"Well," I suggested, "we could always add a high Episcopalian to the group of men in ad No. 2, which would certainly build the campaign spiritual-wise at least for the black and white ads. And for developing the corporate image, why not have Zsa Zsa wear something distinctive . . . say a black eye-patch in every ad?"

"Spavin," bellowed Mr. Leaky in a voice that could swim upstream underwater, "you are an advertising genius. Let's celebrate and go out and get drunk."

Several hours later, Mr. Leaky and I were listing against the bar of the Seepage Happy Interlude Tavern, soused to the gills. We had been drinking Mr. Leaky's favorite cocktail, made up of equal parts of vodka and Kool-aid. They called it the Pipecleaner. The conversation turned to discussing the fair sex.

"Botchwell," said Mr. Leaky, "I played around a lot but I can proudly shay that I never went to bed with my wife before we were married. Did you?"

"I don't know," I answered, "what was her maiden name?"

"Proneville."

"No, Mr. Leaky," I said honestly but with sincere regret, "I can't say I ever did."

"Spavins," he said, "you're one shwell kid, and I'm going to shee to it that you're the new V.P. on the Leaky Septic-Tank account at Pearl & Swine. I never could stand that idiot Fatbucket."

"It's true, Fatty has slipped a lot lately, but he used to be a top executive," I said loyally, remembering that it was Fatbracket who had given me a leg up.

"Yes, my boy, you're on your way to the top. But in the future there's just one request I'd like to make. From now on, wear socks, will 'ya?"

"Sure, Leaky, old top," I said, and slapped him hard on the back, causing him to spill his ninth Pipecleaner. We laughed together.

My advertising career was off the launching pad.

For those interested in the technical side of advertising, and in aspects of its cultural history, I probably should indicate that we later found the black eye-patch device had been used before. After a number of brainstorming sessions, we came up with a similar but quite original attention-getter and suggested that Zsa Zsa do the endorsements wearing a truss. She responded with enthusiasm, and a demand for ninety thousand dollars more. We complied. It was years before anyone could better the device.

A Letter from Home

Despite my first success, there were those early years before the call came. It was mighty disheartening at times. Sustaining me in this time of strife were the letters I received, at least once a year, from Mother.

It seems only fitting in a memoir to share something of the wonderful relationship that can grow up between a mother and a son. Here, below for example, is reproduced the sort of memorable missive that can sustain a lonely youth:

Dear Sir:

Why do you insist on writing home all the time? Every day it's the same thing. Your father and I aren't interested in whatever in the hell it is you're doing, and have stopped opening letters altogether.

Remember, few boys your age have your opportunity. So stop bellyaching. You're alone in New York, with Times Square for a playground.

You mentioned you'd stopped smoking in order to eat. Isn't this a little much? We're having a party next week—I'll send you some butts.

Those cookies you baked and sent last week were delicious. But for Christ's sake, next time, throw in some salad and cold cuts. We can't live on cookies alone.

Please stop writing home for money. Don't tell me you've spent what I sent you last year?—That 30¢ in stamps?

Have you gotten your chest tattooed yet? You promised you would.

And stop imagining you're sick. Just ignore it and those headaches will pass.

As always,
Your loving Mother

P. S. If you're ever in the neighborhood, drop in. Bring one of those nice girls you met at the hotel—the ones that used to live in a trailer outside Fort Dix.

CHAPTER 8

In the advertising business, as in any other, there are many problems. You have to take the good with the bad. One of the chief pitfalls is working with what are known as "creative people." Creative people are not like ordinary, normal folk because they are, first of all, creative. Secondly, they are sneaky. And finally, all creative people are immoral. These minor flaws in their character lead to a wide gulf of differences.

The advertising business is a nervous, hectic, and frustrating type of operation. Everyone is overpaid. One realizes that he couldn't possibly ever get another job at that price if he were fired, which leads to fear, short tempers, and duodenal ulcers. That's why in advertising someone is always getting mad at someone else and losing his temper. Yet it's never referred to just that way. Instead, it's called "letting off a little steam." Executives and creative people let off steam in different ways.

When an executive gets mad, he has several possible courses of action. He sometimes shuts the door to his inner office and kicks the big clubby red-leather chairs that hiss when you sit in them. Or one by one he breaks all the nice, long, shiny, yellow pencils that he has on his desk in a coffee mug given to him mistakenly by *Sports*

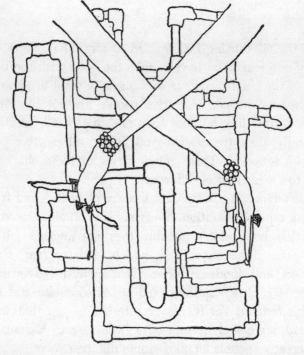

Love Those Pipes

Leaky Septic Tanks

Illustrated. He may then retreat to the executive john and ram his knee ten times into the large metal partition that separates the water closets, pretending it is the client's groin. (This is mainly why they have executive johns. Nothing can be more embarrassing than to do this in the peasants' john and be caught by the mail-room boys or some of the clerks from the accounting department.) Or he can just walk up and down Madison Avenue saying dirty words and kicking over an occasional litter basket.

Creative people, on the other hand, must never let off steam in monastic solitude. A creative person must always inform as many other people as possible that he has blown his top because of some stupid decision or usual bungling by the executives. He will first abuse his or someone else's secretary with loud and profane language; then storm up and down the aisles in Art or Copy (*both,* if he thinks the executives have been extremely stupid or bungling) and inform everyone, those who are not also shouting, that his idea is the only idea that makes sense and why can't the ignorant fools realize it? Some creative people even use loud-speakers.

In this way, creative people let off steam. That's why at the end of the day they are healthy and ruddy and robust, their cheeks are cherry red with joy, knowing that they still have plenty of steam to let off during the meeting in the conference room tomorrow morning. It is only the account executives who run for the 5:34 at night, their hands full of pencil splinters and their knees throbbing from ramming the wall, who have not fully expressed their rage and who feel stifled and suffocated by it all. These are the men who get ulcers and not creative people, who are fulfilled.

My first encounter with creative people at Pearl and Swine was when I called an initial meeting with the Art Director and the Copy Chief. Our principal copy writer, Fairfax Rubicam, arrived first and we shook hands.

"Good morning," I said.

"A cool, crisp, sunny morning to you," said Mr. Rubicam, "and a hearty, warm and friendly welcome to big, successful and impressive Pearl & Swine."

Reginald Original, the Art Director, came in and we shook hands.

"Please excuse my hands," said Original, "but it's early and I haven't had a chance to go to my office yet to put chalk dust and grease pencil on them."

(Many art departments have smudge contests with a prize awarded every afternoon at five o'clock.)

"Well," I said, taking the bull by the horns, "what seems to be the first thing to discuss, gentlemen? Art or Copy?"

"Art," said Reginald Original.

"Copy," Fairfax Rubicam said.

"Gentlemen," I remarked to fill in, "there seems to be something lacking in the ads we are turning out for Leaky. Either of you have any ideas about what's wrong? Where's the fault lie?"

"Art," said Fairfax Rubicam.

"Copy," Reginald Original said.

"Okay," I said, "let's discuss them both. Ruby, as the copy chief on the account, what approach do you think we should use for the new campaign we're planning to run in *Grits* this coming year?"

"The copy should be longer," said Rubicam. "People just don't want to bother to read short copy. And most of the page as it stands is covered by some fool picture of Zsa Zsa Garbo stroking her septic-tank. There isn't any room for more words. *Words* sell products, not pictures. Words, beautiful, flowing, expressive words that dance trippingly on the tongue like a ballerina, and rise up full in the throat like a roe or a young hart; words that ring like churchbells in the dell of a quiet sedate New England village nestled in the amber waves of grain. *Words* sell septic-tanks, and not those goddam pictures of that slut standing there in a truss."

"Like hell," Original said, swinging his T-square. "It's the illustration that sells a product, and not all that dull, hackneyed garbage that Tiresome here writes. What does looking at a picture of a lovely woman make a man think of? Well, if he's a red-blooded American male he thinks of sex, naturally. Banging, screwing, humping, good old-fashioned honest-to-goodness making out. And what is the No. 1 sex symbol to the male consumer according to everyone from Fraud to Ernest Dichtate? Septic-Tanks! That's why the Art is all-important."

"I suppose you're right," I said.

As Original talked, he removed the pictures from my wall and drew a magnificent mural of nearly nude women, clad in nothing but trusses, rolling and tumbling, and laughing as they pinched each other on their pink and fleshy flanks. The man was immensely talented.

"Yes," I admitted, "I'll have to agree that this sort of thing does make me want to go out and buy a tank. But I do feel that we should be thorough in our analysis of our current advertising and aim for the proper balance in copy and layout. This will bring the Leaky Septic-Tank image into sharper focus consumer-wise and should result in boosting the old sales curve like it's never been boosted before. After all, gentlemen, I'm sure that none of us have any pride of authorship that would stand in the way of what our clients' advertising really needs, of what really *sells*, and I know that our petty differences can easily be settled by a friendly—"

My little speech was interrupted when a heavy bronze ash tray hit me in the teeth. All the time I had been talking, Rubicam and Original were waging a vicious fist fight, using any weapons they could grab. I was comforted by the fact that the blow was not really intended for me. As to the fight, Original was easily twice the size of Rubicam, and the latter being at least twenty years older was probably going to come out second best.

"Well, gentlemen," I said, "I guess that about buttons things up for this morning. It is getting mighty close to lunchtime."

Reginald Original and Fairfax Rubicam stopped abruptly. Original slowly lowered the fire tongs and Rubicam released his grip on the other's throat. The frowns that had been on their faces were replaced by the sunny smiles of camaraderie.

"Lunchtime," beamed Original.

"I thought it'd never come," Rubicam added, clasping his arm around Original's shoulder.

"Well, Ruby," asked Reg, "where will it be today? *LIFE* is having a luncheon at the Biltmore."

"Or we could take in the NBC presentation at the Waldorf. They're having a buffet."

"Let's do *both*," they agreed, and before I knew it,

they were racing out of the office, arm in arm. There is only one way to handle creative people and that's to capitalize on their extremely limited span of attention.

Right after lunch, a little after four, we got together again and this time we were mellow and jolly and the like. Not one unpleasant word was spoken for the remainder of the day. And we spitballed it for ten minutes and finally struck oil. We decided on a complete change in the media schedule. Instead of running the whole campaign in *Grits,* we decided on a co-ordinated series of ads in *Vogue, Boys' Life, Unity, Forbes, Cue, Pen Pals, Uncle Billy's Whiz Bang, Punch, Turkey World, Flair, National Geographic,* and *The Christian Science Minotaur.*

This consumer campaign would of course be supplemented by good solid advertising to the trade. We also planned ads to run in *Septic-Tank Age, Sewage Journal, Septic Circular Keytone, Tank Recorder, Flush Engineering, Septic Week,* and a new annual, *It's a Plumber's World.*

Looking back on it, I congratulated myself for having worked so successfully with a creative team. When the ads finally appeared in the magazines (that was the week Mr. Swine almost jumped from the fortieth floor) our client had a well-rounded program at last. In addition to the print schedule, I had also started working with the agency's jingle writer, Gilbert Sullivan, and we came up with a commercial that was soon on the lips of all America. It was sung to the tune of *Yankee Doodle.* You must have heard it.

When your septic-tanks are full
And you need some new ones
Leaky comes in orange, purple,
Yellow, beige and blue ones.

Leaky, Leaky Septic-Tanks
Leaky means more leisure
Leaky, Leaky Septic-Tanks
Are a plumbers' pleasure.

If your septic-tank's worn out
And is old and creaky
Buy a Barbara Fritchie model
Septic-tank by Leaky.

Leaky, Leaky Septic-Tanks
Last a whole lot longer
Does a patriotic job
And keeps our country stronger.

Working closely with Sullivan for several weeks, Gilbert and I got to know each other quite well. Many are the golden afternoons we spent in each other's company, sometimes working shoulder to shoulder on the new jingle, sometimes just chewing the breeze. It was during one of these sessions he opened up and told his life story. I never realized how much two dissimilar men could have in common. Pulling up a big red-leather club chair, I leaned back to listen as the events of his life were opened before me like the true drama it was.

"Well," he said, "you won't believe this. No one ever does. It's too preposterous. It all began when my great-grandfather came to America from Ireland, during the whiskey famine in 1848, to work as a page boy in a

New York bank. For forty years he worked as a page boy, working long hours for low wages. There were few rewards except status. Yet what was status without money, thought my great-grandfather. So he scrimped and saved for the forty years and retired from the bank, planning then to buy his own business. The problem was what sort of business to buy.

"While at the bank, one of his myriad duties was to put out fresh clean blotters every day. Man, did that bank ever use blotters—hundreds, thousands, millions of them.

"That was it! He would buy a blotter factory and perfect a new, vastly improved blotter and get rich. Checking the classified section of Harold Greeley's New York *Harold Tribune*, his search was rewarded. A blotter factory was for sale in Johnstown, Pennsylvania.

"My great-grandfather's blotter business was an overnight success, and he soon became known as the Blotter Baron of Johnstown. His factory was enlarged again and again and his giant warehouses were filled to the brim with Sullivan Super-Sop blotters. The year was 1888.

"Then came the blizzard. Transportation in and out of Johnstown was impossible. The factory kept running and inventory piled up. Every available warehouse, storehouse, barn, and bin was stocked from floor to ceiling with blotters.

"When spring came, the snow melted. It created the Johnstown Flood of 1889. Water poured down the mountain sides and into the city. It covered all, partially submerging the Sullivan Super-Sop Blotter Factory, until a strange thing happened. The superior quality of the blotters began to manifest itself. Water streamed into the factory and the adjacent warehouses, storehouses, barns, and bins. The blotters absorbed the water and swelled to double and triple their normal size. They worked beautifully for a time and finally the walls of the factory could withstand the strain no longer. Something had to give.

"It did. The factory literally exploded. Blotter lint covered the city of Johnstown in the shadow of a huge mushroom cloud. The fallout was unbelievable in its proportions. Some of the lint was found in the pockets of tweed suits as far west as South Bend, Indiana.

"Well, that did it. Great-grandfather went back to being a page boy at the bank. He married, settled down, and raised a family. He even bought a harpsichord, and every evening he and the missus and all the kids would gather around and sing Irish songs. They became well-known.

"Eventually, they went into vaudeville. Their eldest son, my grandfather, sang heart-ringing solos, and there was never a dry eye in the house when he put his Irish tenor into *Pool Balls are the Devil's Rosary*.

"Then *he* grew up and got married and raised a family who were, every one, musically gifted. My father, Ed, originated the variety show. He was also the first man to sing *If* by Rudyard Kipling, accompanying himself by playing the tuba with his nose.

"Of his ten children, nine had beautiful voices. I was the tenth, and totally tone-deaf. Can't sing a note, play as much as a washboard, or carry a tune in a bucket. My parents, nevertheless, sent me to Harvard to major in music. The drama professor, Mr. Groundling, was nonetheless delighted to find a boy named Gilbert Sullivan, and almost before I knew it, I was a member of the Instant Pudding Club, starring in their musicals. After every performance the audience would come backstage and pelt me with stones and garbage. I was miserable.

"Then, I met Mercedes Mikado, who is now Mrs. Sullivan. She is also the talented mother of our four talented sons, better known as the greatest male quartet in show business, the Ick Spots.

"We live up in Scarsdale, where my father-in-law, Moss Mikado, is a producer of amateur theatricals. Just because my name is what it is, I'm playing the lead tonight in their musical presentation of *My Fair Lady*. I just *can't* go through with it. I can't walk out on the stage in that damn beige cardigan, singing *The Rine in Spine is Minely in the Pline*."

"Absurd title," I said.

"It isn't much of a song," said Gilbert, "and what's worse, I sing it miserably. Poor George."

"George?" I asked.

"He wrote the original play on which the musical was based, called *Androcles and the Dreyfuss Fund*.

"Well, Gilbert," I said, "it's quite a story. But you have to take it philosophically. After all it's only an amateur presentation. So what if it kills some of your leisure hours?"

"That's just it," he moaned. "With rehearsals and all, it's too time-consuming. I don't have any time to complete my project."

"Project?" I asked.

"Yes," he said, his beady little eyes growing warm

with genuine pleasure. "I've been working on it for years. You should see it. I'm making a life-size bust of Eileen Farrell out of old bank blotters."

See what I mean about creative people?

CHAPTER 9

As you read this book, you are no doubt concluding that such a life is limited, stepping off the Coolidge College campus right onto Madison Avenue to work for Pearl & Swine. Yet, nothing could be farther from the truth. Not long ago I took a vacation, a genuine adventure in international understanding.

Here's how I happened to go to Europe. One morning I was reading the classified section of the New York Times, the only section I ever read, and happened to stumble on a very interesting ad which read as follows:

For Sale—2nd hand book—*How to Get Around in South America*. Has never been taken out of U.S. Call Mrs. C. B. Luce,[1] Ju 6-1212

Hmmm, I said, that's my trouble. I don't get around enough. Instead of going to the office that morning, I went to Europe.

Now I'm not going to bore you with talk about a lot of ruins and museums and the like. One evening in Moscow I had nothing to do, and having a TV set in my room at the hotel, I consulted *Pravda* for the evening program,[2] which read as follows:

[1] Be sure to read her column in *McCall's*—"Without Porfirio."
[2] Not nearly as good as France's *TV Gide*

7:00	Nastasha Navashnik
7:30	I Reported Mama
8:00	Lawrence Welt
8:30	Fibber McGee and Molotov
9:00	What's My Fine?
9:30	Take it or Else
10:00	Concentration Camp
10:30	Truth or Siberia

Promptly at seven o'clock I tuned in. *Nastasha Navashnik, Soviet Wife* was a soap opera that asked the question: "Can a poor little peasant girl from starving mining town in Siberia be happy married to a filthy rich American capitalist?" The answer, of course, was *nyet*.

The introductory commercial was designed to sell Siberian Snow Tires. Naturally, it was of particular interest. "Comrades," said the announcer, "it now July, and winter be here two weeks. Better hurry and get your Siberian Snow Tires. Drivers of U.S.S.R., unite! You have nothing to lose but your chains.

"And now *Nastasha Navashnik, Soviet Wife*."

In a short time I found myself completely absorbed. It seemed that the last episode left Nastasha lying ill in the Vladivostock hospital, a victim of a socialistic disease. She had just had relapse. Relapse weighed 6 pounds, 4 rubles.

Father of the child was not her shiftless lazy husband, Nogoodnik Navashnik (obviously rich old American capitalist), but her lover, Boris Borsht, the shortstop for Cincinnatski Reds.

Boris pays a call to Nastasha in her sickroom and brings her a bouquet of *steppes* and lump of Cuban sugar. He asks her how she, a sexy woman of only fifty summers, can be happy married to man twice her age. Nastasha admits she has felt old age creeping up on her.

At this point, program was refreshingly interrupted by commercial.

"Comrades, have you tried Communism lately? If you haven't, you may be missing something—like your family. And now back to *Nastasha Navashnik, Soviet Wife.*"

Boris is sitting on edge of her hospital bed making violent love to her, trying to slip his hand inside her *samovar.* As Boris still has sugar all over his hands, Nastasha does her best to repel his advances. At that moment in walks her husband, Mr. Navashnik, looking strangely like Henry Ford, and surprises two lovers.

Not being understanding husband, he creates scene and strong language is exchanged by both sides. Nogoodnik suggests duel but Boris invokes his power of veto. Nogoodnik leads with right cross to nose, and Boris retaliates with smart combination to *cossack.* They are at it hammer and sickle when Nastasha leaps into fray and helps Boris smother her hubby with rubber sheet. They bind him with tube from enema bag and flush him down *volga.* Nurse enters room and reminds Nastasha that she not supposed to be out of bed.

Another commercial.

"Comrades, have you tried Pavlov's Caviar? Is caviar that makes the mouth water, as you spread it easily on your hard, dry *vodka.* Is prepared and packed by beautiful Russian girls, why it spreads so easily." This message was followed by a picture of trademark, Elsie the Pavlov sturgeon. Back to Nastasha.

Nurse put Nastasha back to bed and suddenly noticed that rubber sheet was missing. So Nasty and Boris had to let Nurse in on gag and told her all about dead husband. Nurse said she'd never reveal secret because Nogoodnik has several times pinched her on the *kremlin* and she is glad rich capitalistic bastard got what was coming to him.

So Nasty, Boris, and Nurse all laughed up a storm, and Nasty rips a few stitches, as curtain fell and omnipresent organ music crescendoed.

Was then brief commercial by alternate sponsor, Aunt Jeminski's Black Bread Mix, saying just "to add water and try not to be disappointed." This was followed by reminder to watch other program, *Vulva, the Vulgar Volgan,* on another network.

Because of fascinating Russian TV, and sturdy guards outside the door, I hardly ever left the hotel.

Experience in Italy was equally rewarding. The news of my arrival preceded me by several hours, so that when I arrived in Rome thousands of cheering foreigners were on hand to meet my plane. It must be explained however that they were expecting someone else and when I appeared on the balcony that evening and made the sign of the cross, I was pelted by stones and garbage from the lusty demonstrative throng. It ruined the new smooth suit I had bought that afternoon at Sacco & Vanzetti's.

Yet, Italy was wonderful—the culture, the atmosphere, the charm—no country can compare with it. It might not have plumbing but it certainly has many tumbled-down buildings. Still, the plumbing situation is appalling. I attempted to imitate the native custom but without success, even though I tried to look casual and even whistled. The embarrassment was unbearable and I felt about as conspicuous as a nun with a Nixon button.

Perhaps the most impressive thing about Italy is its churches. My guide took me to many of them, and they could only be described as architectural masterpieces. The Italians have great reverence for their churches, and with the exception of a few hawkers of souvenirs, they never go inside at all. This privilege they reserve politely for tourists.

"Tell me, Benito," I said to one guide, "doesn't a devout Italian ever see his priest at all?"

"Si," said Benito in a bit of striking folk wisdom, "three times in a lifetime. When he is born, when he is confirmed, and when he is married."

I mused. "An Italian in America does pretty much the same," I said finally, "only the three occasions when he sees his priest are when he is confirmed, when he is married, and when he is electrocuted." The guide became abusive. Later, when I experienced some difficulty in getting around, I found that he had marked me with a curious caste mark, signaling to all that I was an untouchable.

While in Italy I managed to uncover some very interesting facts about the death of Julius Caesar. Being in the advertising business it was of prime concern to me and I prepared a short article on the subject which I sold easily to the Roman literary magazine, *La Appalachin*. Here is the article, convincing proof that I write as well on foreign affairs as on domestic relations:

The Death of Caesar
BY BOSWELL SPAVINS

Most people think that Caesar died as a result of a heinous stabbing by one Brutus. Nothing could be farther from the truth.

Caesar really died as a result of taking an overdose of a product that was a tincture of sulphur and molasses called chemically the Ides of March.

The Ex-Libris Pharmaceutical Company almost went broke on the bad publicity and had to find a new brand name for their product. Short snappy ones, like Vel, Mum, Tide, Ban, Dash, Fab, Amo, Amas, Amat, were in vogue. So they decided the new name would be SCRAM.

A motivation research institute tested consumer acceptance on SCRAM with house-to-house interviews, which indicated that the product needed an all-around face-lifting.

Their hastily coined slogan couldn't miss. "SCRAM—the laxative that gets into the blood stream twice as fast as Dracula!" (Incidentally, the best slogan today is said to be "Smoke Rosser Reefs—the only cigarette guaranteed to cure cancer.")

SCRAM needed a brand image also,—like Bert and Vincent Piel. A new advertising agency was appointed (Battus, Bartic, Domino and Octavius) and the SCRAM campaign "was off and running in high gear," as the Account Executive so put it.

Yet the SCRAM sales curve continued to fall and the

SCRAM "group" at the agency said the product needed "greater impact at the flagpole level." They struck upon an idea that would make or break SCRAM, one that should "practically revamp the marketing concept laxative-wise," said the agency head.

Thus it happened. INSTANT SCRAM was introduced in December, A.D. 475, for the Christmas promotion.

In A.D. 476—Rome fell.

From Italy I went directly to Paris, the city of eternal spring. It's very difficult to be in Paris and not be in love. In Paris, everyone everywhere was in love. In fact, it got to be damned disconcerting. Back home folks just *sit* on the park benches.

The best thing about Paris is the wine. I tasted many different kinds, the humble good local wines of the provinces, and the great wines from Burgundy, Chanel, and Givenchy to Lanvin and Cabinet. The best wines anywhere of course are imported, and I was smart enough not to let the French pawn off their domestic stuff on me. I can still see their faces when I'd wave off their rosé and insist on Manischewitz.

Well, all good trips must come to an end so I sailed from Le Harve on the *Wilson Victory* and in fourteen days (the Captain still insisted on zigzagging, although everyone told him the war was over) we were saluting the Statue of Liberty in the New York Harbor.

I could hardly wait to get off the boat, to stroll on my beloved Madison Avenue. It was a beautiful, balmy July day and just as I was passing Brooks Brothers a really amusing thing happened: a pleasant summer breeze sent a cinder stabbing into my left eye. This might not seem terribly amusing to you, but I marveled, as the odds against this happening are phenomenal. I thought of the fact that there are 8,000,000 left eyes in New York. The chances of a cinder finding mine were almost uncanny. I vowed to keep it always. Laughing at this comical happenstance, the cinder was removed by surgery after a day or two, and once back at the apartment, I placed it under my pocket microscope.

Just as I had suspected, this was no happenstance at all. A cheery message was inscribed on the cinder, a cunning bit of promotion. "New York," it read, "is a Summer Festival."

CHAPTER 10

"Well, Stupid," barked Mr. Leaky, as he paced back and forth in his large office at the Leaky Corporation, "how do we expect to sell septic-tanks to the right people if we don't know who the people are who *use* septic-tanks?"

He lashed me across the withers with the riding crop he always carried under his arm for the purpose. Mr. Leaky was of the old school, and believed in corporate punishment.

"What we really need is some market research," he suggested, lashing away. "We ought to find out more about this dynamic septic-tank market. Who *buys* septic-tanks, who uses them the *most* and *why*, what does the average septic-tank user think about and talk about, what're his politics and his religion, what is his income, and what are his hopes and dreams? In other words, let's get an accurate profile of the typical tank consumer and make a study of him so detailed in every respect that we know our market cold."

I applauded loudly, but Mr. Leaky struck out at me again with his crop.

"Well," I said, "we do know that many of our customers live in hotels or apartments. These are people who used to live in the country and moved to the city and still buy a tank for sentimental reasons."

"Bull!" Leaky shouted. "Get out and be back here next week with a complete and comprehensive market research report—or I'll be wearing your ears for cuff links."

I got out, as I have always been especially proud of my ears.

When I got back to the office at Pearl & Swine, I telephoned a man who, in the opinion of the advertising world, is the leader in the great and growing field of market research. I told him what we wanted, a master profile of the typical tank user by next week, and hung up before he had a chance to protest. If this man couldn't get the market story in a week, I was doomed.

I was not disappointed. On Friday, my secretary announced that he was outside my office with a full report.

"Send him in!" I cried. A great sigh of gratitude swept over me.

Pollitz Keyhole, chairman of Scuttlebutt, Inc., was indeed a research man in every respect. Even as a young man back in the twenties, he had proved by the use of calculus and a slide rule that it was actually 23.4 Skidoo. After college, he became interested in the marketing of chess sets and became one of the largest chess dealers in the trade. He specialized further and, with the help of research, found that chess players prefer to buy certain pieces separately through middlemen and so became the first pawnbroker in America. He later married the lovely Cotangent Starch, and they lived happily in the back room of his little pawnshop on Wall Street.

"Key," I said, rising, "this is indeed a pleasure."

Keyhole's report was worthy of his reputation and then some. After my call, he had set his field workers loose interviewing thousands of individuals all over the world. The results were impressive.

The report showed clearly that the average septic-tank user is between the ages of three and sixty-eight, lives in a one-family dwelling in a household of more than one sex. He tends to be more urban than rural in the densely populated areas. The average user is either male or female depending on sex, is both political and religious, and tended to be more wealthy in the upper income brackets but poorer in the low. His use of the septic-tank varied in direct proportion to the amount of time he spent at home, with the exception of bashful individuals.

At the end of the report, the findings were computed, tabulated, collated, analyzed, and defined. It stated that the "most used" septic-tank was found in Vladivostock hospital and was stopped up. (A plumber finally found the trouble and removed a body who, according to the report, was a dead ringer for Henry Ford).

It was an interesting report, if you like market research, and it certainly cleared up a myriad of questions that we at Pearl & Swine had only wondered about for years. You can't beat good solid field work when it comes to "capturing the profile of consumer usage, septic-tank-wise," as I have often heard Mr. Fatbracket say. Yes, the report was a good one and I happily wrote a check for $40,000 and handed it to Keyhole.

"Key," I said, "it gives me great pleasure to award you this small fee, and let me say that I speak for both Pearl

& Swine and our client when I promise you that our
fervent respect and good wishes go with it."

Mr. Keyhole was apparently choked with emotion. He
just snatched the check and left hurriedly.

It was Friday afternoon; I still had time to catch the
train up to Seepage. I could hardly wait until I handed
Mr. Leaky the report. Leaky slowly read it, seeming to
soak up its valuable contents and memorize every perti-
nent fact. When at last he had finished the report, he
looked up. The perpetual frown on his face had changed
from the nose down into a leer.

"Good-by, Translux," he said softly.

The Translux-Tank Company was our competition,
and I could tell from the menace in his voice that Mr.
Leaky was planning, by the use of this new information,
to force them off the supermarket shelves and out of business. Mr. Leaky was happy as a lark.

"Spavins," said Mr. Leaky, standing up and putting a
rough hand on my shoulder, "this is just what we're looking for. With information like this we can revamp our
marketing concepts, swallow up our competition in merg-
ers, and double our prices. What say we celebrate over
a couple of Pipecleaners at the old Happy-Interlude
Tavern?"

As we sipped, Mr. Leaky once again put a hairy arm
around me. "Boswell," he said, "you are going to be one
helluva success in the ad game. Madison Avenue needs
men like you, *for a better world through bigger profits
through advertising.*"

I can't remember ever having the Ad Council's slogan
touch me as deeply, and Mr. Leaky's interpretation gave

it new dimension and meaning. His riding crop had fallen to the floor and he slowly kicked it away.

It was then I knew that not all the satisfactions were in pleasing the client. I had earned a friend.

CHAPTER 11

Wham!

Mr. Swine's official Boy Scout hatchet bit deeply into the long mahogany table in the conference room.

"Hard sell!" he said. "That's what this needs, and not all those Garbo girls and movie stars sitting around stripped admiring a septic-tank. Let's flush this new fangled corporate image bullroar and get back to good old belly-to-counter selling. We got to get the kind of stuff my nephew Ted runs for that pill account of his— 'Guaranteeed to cure hoof rot in thirty to sixty days or double your money back!' That's the type of thinking we need to upgrade this rotten campaign."

He was looking right at me.

"Why, just yesterday," Mr. Swine continued, "I was over at Ted's agency, and he showed me one of his new TV spots for those hoof rot pills. Shows a diagram of a steer's stomach. The pills are a combination of ingredients and enter the belly in soft tiny flakes, like a doctor's prescription, to fight depression and calm a steer's jittery nerves fast fast fast. Yes, sir, that's what I call good old knock 'em, sock 'em, hard-hitting advertising. Makes a man proud he's in the business."

He whipped out a big banner that read "CAVEAT

EMPTOR" and marched around the room playing a fife and limping slightly, while we all applauded until our arms ached.

"We could create a brand image for the product," I said, "like Lizzie the Borden cow."

Mr. Swine ignored my remark.

"Anyone have an intelligent suggestion?"

"Well," said Mr. Pearl, "we could always hire six beautiful models and hold a contest every year to elect one Miss Leaky Septic-Tank."

"We could have the ads showing the winner posing with the product," I said. "And for a catchy slogan she could say, 'My septic-tank is Leaky, the *dry* septic-tank.'"

"I don't want to throw cold water over anybody's idea but does anyone have any contributions germane to the problem?" asked Mr. Pearl, pouring a glass of cold water and dumping it slowly over my head. "If not, the meeting is adjourned."

"Yes," added Mr. Swine, "enough of all of this moronic talk about creativity. Let's get some hard sell into this campaign. That's all. Meeting's over."

Two minutes later I was back in my office thinking about hard sell. I reached for my dictionary and looked up *hard*. "Severe, harsh, difficult, arduous, laborious, tedious, and repellent." I thought about them all and finally decided that "repellent" was what Mr. Swine probably meant. "Repellent," it said, is something "revolting, sickening, disgusting, nauseating, offending, obnoxious, unendurable, nasty, loathesome, and vile." At last, I knew exactly what Mr. Swine wanted, and what was so obviously missing in the present Leaky Septic-Tank campaign.

Naturally, I called in Fax Rubicam again.

"Okay," Ruby said, "what's on your mind, other than that pounding, splitting headache undoubtedly caused by tension tension tension?"

He punctuated his words by hitting my head with a tiny hammer.

"We've got to get some hard sell into the campaign," I said, "because if we don't Mr. Swine's ax will be on my neck instead of the conference table. I'm counting on you to put some guts in our copy story and push the old sales curve up into orbit."

"Okay," said Ruby, "it's done. Account's a headache? You'll be glad you called for Fax Rubicam. Believe me, friends, there's nothing better. Accept no substitutes."

About a week later, the phone rang. It was Ruby. He had the new hard sell ideas for the account. How would I like to come down to the TV viewing room to a screening of his most recent creativity? Would I? Such was my confidence that I invited Mr. Swine, who happened to be in the office at the time, sitting on my chest. We were down there in a thrice, Ruby cut the lights, and the new commercials flashed on the dummy TV screen.

The film showed a lovely white colonial house, complete with wagon wheels and an eagle over the door. Our background music was pastoral, heavy on flutes, and the announcer's voice suggested that we look in on this New England home "nestled in the foothills of residential serenity." We did. But the serenity was all on the surface! Underneath the ground was a sludge-filled septic-tank, and the screen showed us a cross-section diagram. The tank was seething with discontent, a vat of angry lava, as the music suddenly swelled to dramatic pitch.

"Now what would happen," asked the announcer, "if the tank *backed up?*" His voice was menacing. A clash of cymbals on the audio and suddenly the family of two adults, six children, and three dogs poured from the house, screaming. The announcer's face appeared: "Is your septic-tank BACK-UPPITY?" Angry lava poured out of the house through every door and window, and the eagle over the door shrieked and flew away.

Then, the same comfortable homestead was shown. Beneath it, a Leaky Septic-Tank this time. The family was happy and the eagle flew back. Our cross-section diagram showed how sewage enters a Leaky Septic-Tank in soft tiny flakes. Not a powder, not a grind, but millions of tiny sewage buds which made a Leaky Septic-Tank "last good to the last drop." The flutes played *Home, Sweet Home*, Bert Parks came on briefly, singing *There She Is, Miss America*, and the family pledged allegiance to the flag. The commercial ended.

Mr. Swine and I and everyone there applauded until our hands were raw and bleeding. And Ruby thought we would never stop slapping him on the back for a job well done. Mr. Swine had gotten out his handkerchief.

"It's beautiful," he said, "beautiful."

CHAPTER 12

Pearl & Swine was a maelstrom of activity. All of us on the Leaky account were busily preparing ads to follow the announcement being released from Seepage. The big news was that Leaky had stolen a march on the competition, and was departing from the manufacture of standard-size tanks. Leaky was bringing out a whole new line of *compacts*.

The new Leaky Rumbler would be smaller, less expensive, easier to maintain, and a cinch to repair. It promised durability, more mileage on fewer gallons. The Rumbler would be plain in color with very little trim and no chrome at all. But the salient feature was that the pump motor would no longer be in the front, but in the back.

When ads were completed, the problem was through what media should they meet the public. We had a choice of newspapers, magazines, direct mail, outdoor, bus cards, matchbook covers, walking sandwich-board men, even skywriting. Finally deciding that our vehicle would be magazines, it boiled down to a decision between two leading publications. Both were invited to make presentations at Pearl & Swine.

The presentation is a sensible, orderly, and factual

description of a medium's merits. As competition has increased for the advertising dollar, some presentations have become more elaborate. But the best of them are straightforward and believable.

The first was made by the representative for *Plowboy* magazine. As you know, *Plowboy* is a pin-up periodical specifically edited for the rural housewife. Much of the editorial content is devoted to articles about the canning of vegetables, removing manure stains, and what to do until the vet comes.

Plowboy, however, does have its lighter side. The current issue, to cite an example, concerned itself with the emaciated cattle of Mexico. Colorful illustrations showed numberless bony beasts sprawled on the parched earth, dying from hoof-and-mouth disease. Intermingled with the dead cattle were members of the Hollywood clan who had flown down just for kicks. The photography was beautiful. The rep said that the reader response from this article was overwhelming. From as far away as Formosa and Poland, women sent CARE packages to the group in Hollywood.

He also pointed out that since the marketing objective of our client was to reach people living in rural areas who would be progressive enough to buy a Leaky Septic-Tank and up their status, his magazine was tailor-made. By the use of several interesting charts and graphs, which included enlarged replicas of his high-school diploma and honorable discharge from the marines, he proved beyond a reasonable doubt that the *Plowboy* audience could be defined as an eager to buy, eager to try group of agrarian matriarchs.

It was certainly an impressive presentation.

The next day, another one was given by Bud Bleeding-heart, who represented a revered inspirational publication, the *Mackeral Digest*. Bud, a full-blooded Rednecki Indian, gave us the pitch garbed in war paint and feathers. He began by exposing us to the romantic historical background of the magazine.

There had once been a medicine man named Moe Mackerelsnapping who was the beloved spiritual leader of his tribe. Even as a boy, Moe was interested in journalism and told everyone that when he became a man he intended to be a publisher. Moe grew up to be a strong, stout brave, but before he could pursue a career in journalism he became involved with the wayward daughter of the local feed store keeper, a charmer called Novena Farina.

Late each evening, Moe and Novena would steal softly in through the back door of her father's feed store to make mad passionate love. One night Mr. Farina returned to the store to pick up his copy of *If* by Rudyard Kipling. He happened to hear giggles of ecstasy coming from the backroom. Grabbing his shotgun, Mr. Farina raced to the back of the building and there before his very eyes were the two lovers in a compromising position, lodged in fervent embrace between the fertilizer and the laying mash. At the insistence of Mr. Farina's shotgun, and with the help of a local justice of the peace, the two were made one.

Yet even after the nuptial knot was tied, Moe and Novena continued their nocturnal revelries in the back of the feed store. Now that they were married and, as they said, "legal," their shouts and screams of uninhibited glee kept the neighborhood awake into the wee hours.

The situation proved embarrassing to Mr. Farina so eventually he decided to take matters into his own hands. Quite unbeknownst to Moe or Novena, he invited the great French evangelist, Billy Dimanche, to hold an evening revival in the back of the feed store, complete with hymn singing and all.

The worshipers came by the score from miles around to gather in the back of the store. Following the quiet but forceful instructions of Billy Dimanche the lights were turned off, the whole congregation sat silently on the grain bags in the darkness and meditated. Soon, the back door opened. In sneaked Moe and Novena in their customary manner. It didn't take them long to engage in their favorite act. The silence was pierced by a happy cry from Moe and a pained but pleasured yip from Novena. It was then that Mr. Farina turned on the lights.

No one could have been more astonished than Billy Dimanche and his throng of worshipers. Billy recovered his composure in an instant. Opening his prayer book he preached one of the longest and most inspirational sermons in history. Yet it was difficult for Billy to hold the interest of the congregation because Moe and Novena never once even paused in their ardent endeavors. In fact, at one point in the sermon Billy had to walk over to the lovers and place a foot atop their heaving flanks to quiet them.

Along about the end of the preaching, a strange phenomenon occurred. The lovers stilled, then separated. Moe and Novena began to sit up and take notice.

Well, the upshot of the matter was that Moe and Novena were saved and Moe became not only a great spiritual leader of the tribe but a brilliant journalist as well. His wife, Novena, was his constant inspiration. Together they initiated the *Mackerel Digest*. Their editorials denounced birth control and self-control with equal gusto. Their how-to articles were renowned. And that was how Moe Mackerelsnapping and his beloved Novena started the *Digest*, and nurtured it until it became the great guidepost of daily living that it is today.

Bud Bleedingheart made it clear that the readers of this publication are still staunch believers in sitting and meditating, are very slow readers in fact, and deemed it as a "must" magazine for our account. He ended the presentation by reciting a few lines of poetry in memory of Moe Mackerelsnapping, his poise and his blind devotion to whatever he was doing:

> *"If you can keep your head*
> *When all the world about you*
> *Is losing theirs, etc. etc."*

"Well," said Mr. Pearl when Bud had ended, "that was a mighty impressive presentation, and I can tell you right now that I personally am in favor of taking the whole advertising appropriation and putting every penny into *Mackerel Digest*.

"Mr. Pearl," I said, "I've made my own media analysis of the situation and I recommend that we give *Mackerel Digest* every consideration. But professionally, I feel as though the weight of evidence seems to favor *Plowboy*. Based on the Politz study of—"

Two days later I presented our media plan to Mr. Leaky up at Seepage.

"Mr. Leaky," I said, "as you can see we recommend

putting the entire budget in *Mackerel Digest*. Both Mr. Pearl and I agree that this magazine reaches an audience tailor-made for septic-tanks. Their reader profiles show that the typical *Digest* subscriber is poor, ignorant, dirty, and meditative."

"Well," said Mr. Leaky, knitting his brow, "maybe. Just let me make one quick telephone call."

He dialed a number.

"It's Lester," he said, "the agency is here. They want us to put the whole budget into *Mackerel Digest*. Okay?"

Even sitting across the room, I could hear the tirade at the other end of the line. Tough as he was, Mr. Leaky had to hold the telephone receiver at arms length to spare his ear. It was obviously someone he regarded as his superior. But since it could be presumed that Mr. Leaky owned the company, who could it be?

My question was soon answered. He hung up and faced me apologetically.

"That was Grandmother. She still owns controlling interest in the corporation, despite the fact that she's eighty-nine. She says nix on the *Mackerel Digest*."

"What does she suggest?" I asked.

"Grandmother wants to put on her own media presentation at Pearl & Swine next week," he said. "Set up a date and I'll bring her into town."

We were all seated around the long oak table in the conference room of Pearl & Swine when Mr. Leaky entered with his grandmother. Lucretia Leaky was a tiny, delicate old lady who carried a gnarled cane. Over her shoulders she wore a lace shawl and perched on her tiny hat was a stuffed bird. She walked briskly to the chair at the head of the table while her grandson sat meekly off to one side.

"Gentlemen," she chirped in her shaky but melodic voice, "you have made a media evaluation, I gather."

We nodded.

"And you've come up with some thingamubob called *Mackerel Digest.*"

We nodded.

"I hereby veto the recommendation for one excellent reason," she said. "It's my money."

"Of course," smiled Mr. Pearl, as we all nodded.

"I wanted *Plowboy* all the time," I said, and Mr. Swine hit me in the teeth with a heavy bronze ash tray.

"But we recommended *Mackerel Digest,*" said Mr. Pearl, "to get some extra *sell* into the campaign."

"Bosh and fiddlesticks," said Mrs. Leaky. "You quacks would recommend anything and that dang fool grandson of mine would approve it."

Mr. Leaky smiled weakly.

"You young scalawags don't know what the word *sell* means. Seventy years ago, when I was in Chicago—"

"Grandmother," said Mr. Leaky, "you *promised.*"

"Shush up," she barked, rapping him smartly with her cane. "As I said, back in those days we knew what *sell* meant. Competition was stiff—but I was running my own house by the time I was twenty-five. That was the year I met your grandfather."

Mr. Leaky bit his nails.

"He was a young space salesman for the leading woman's magazine of the era, *The McCall Girl's Home Journal.* He was soliciting door to door to get folks to advertise. He stayed with us for about a week, and showed us how we could increase our business with some merchandising.

"'Never underestimate the *McCall Girl's* Use-Tested Seal in presenting girls to tentative customers,'" he always said."

We all nodded.

"It really worked. The sales graph that hung in my office went up up up. Shows how some mighty good old-fashioned merchandising can make an enterprise git up and go.

"And you should have seen our house ads. They sure did show up bright and spanking in the shelter books, too.

"Lestoil and I married soon after. I sold the house to that young Adler girl and with the money we started the Leaky Septic-Tank Corps. Never did regret going legit. But tarnation, what we had in those days was a heap of marketing know-how that got us started. So I say let's put the whole dag-burned budget into *The McCall Girl's Home Journal.* Any magazine that runs an entire four-color spread on garbage cans is bound to do the same thing with septic tanks."

We all nodded.

She sat down quickly, somewhat out of breath, and fanned herself with a little lace hanky lightly scented with sachet.

"But Mrs. Leaky," I protested after some thought, "the rep hasn't even taken us to lunch."

The familiar bronze ash tray shattered into my teeth again.

"We'll give it a try, Mrs. Leaky, you can be sure of that," smiled Mr. Pearl. "The new announcement ads for the Leaky Rumbler will go into the magazine of your choosing."

We all nodded.

"You bet your boots it will," she tweeted. "I need you about as much as a pig needs pockets. So tend to your knittin' or I'll change agencies faster than I change my drawers. Come, Lester."

She and her grandson marched out of the conference room.

We stopped nodding.

CHAPTER 13

Long ago and far away I dreamed a dream one day. And now that dream is here beside me, I thought. That's the way my thoughts often ran, to the lyric. I was admiring the robust and healthy state of my little green bankbook. It was a thing of beauty, all those little zeros that mean so much when preceded by a number. It was good to be alive.

During lunch hour I left Pearl & Swine and strolled down Madison Avenue to the Feelings Mutual & Loan where I did my banking. The bank was founded over a century ago and has been "serving the thrifty since 1850" without interruption. Except for a daring holdup made by Boldface Bodoni and his gang, its reputation has been as sound and conservative as the generations of Feelings men who have managed it over the years.

So into the bank I sauntered, walked up to the first window and shoved in my little green bank book. Mr. Bonwit, the teller, was his usual smiling self.

"Well, well," he purred as he picked up the bank book, "another big deposit again this week, young man?"

"No," I announced, "no deposit at all. In fact I'm here to make a withdrawal."

"All right," said Mr. Bonwit, less exuberantly. He

pouted a bit and ripped up some old money. "How much?"

This was the moment I had been waiting for. All those long hours of toil on the farm, my struggle to get through college, and my earnest devotion to Pearl & Swine had at last paid off. And now the time had come.

"All of it," I said. "Every penny."

I thought Mr. Bonwit was going to faint dead away right on the spot. He pleaded with me, begged if you will, even consulted with Mr. Feelings to find out if he could stop me, but it was no use. At last he finally assented, counted out the exact amount of cash several times, and slid it to me under the bars on the cold, marble counter.

"There you are," he said, mopping perspiration from his classic brow with a neatly folded white handkerchief. "Eleven dollars and ten cents."

Perhaps I should explain here that all the advertising people on Madison Avenue live beyond their incomes. They are always up to their narrow lapels in debts and mortgages. Rather than depositers, they are borrowers. That is why my eleven dollars and ten cents represented one of the larger accounts. Small wonder Mr. Bonwit and Mr. Feelings clung to each other as I pocketed the money and walked out of the bank into the fresh clean air.

I turned the wheel of the Rolls-Royce smoothly as the big black car rounded the last curve and the little town of Weedville, New York, came into view. For only eleven dollars and ten cents, Mr. Fatbracket had jumped at the chance. He rented me his car so I could go back to the old home town and impress everyone. I could hardly contain myself with anticipation, driving down familiar streets, hearing the sound of my native language, of looking up childhood pals and snubbing them. After cruising down Main Street several times I headed homeward, where the warm and loving arms of Paw and Maw would be waiting.

As I parked the Rolls in front of the old house, I could see them standing on the porch waving. You can bet that it didn't take me long to grab my suitcase and dash up the driveway, lightly leaping over the dead dogs. And then I was in my mother's arms and Paw was pumping my hand.

"You look thin," said Maw, "I don't think that stork food agrees with you. What you need is a laxative."

She hurried off in the direction of the medicine chest.

"Son," said Paw, "I can't wait to take ya down to the barn and show ya the new herd. But no tricks now," he said, giving me a healthy belt on the ear with his pitchfork. He was still sore about that little prank I had played on his old herd, the group with the suicidal tendencies.

Boy, what a supper dear old Maw put on the table that evening. The board was groaning. I'd helped Paw do the chores first and so I really dug in to the huge bowl of weevils with plenty of grits, the ragweed salad, the candied sweetbreads. I topped it off with a big slice of lemming meringue pie. We could hardly move when we finally pushed back our plates. While Maw cleared the dishes, I helped Paw rebury the silver. Then, after we'd put up our shovels in the shed and were strolling up toward the house, I put my arm around Paw's knobby old shoulder.

"Well, there's gonna be a full moon tonight. S'pose you're going to look up your old girl friend, Cashmere Holstein," Paw said, cupping his hands impulsively. I nodded in silence, but my blood raced and my heart pounded at the thought.

Parking the Rolls-Royce in front of Cashmere's house on Elm Street, I gave the usual three toots on the horn. A bleak thought crossed my mind: perhaps she would not be glad to see me, as I had foolishly forgotten to say good-by to her when I left Weedville for college. But my fears soon vanished as I saw the door open and Cashmere came jiggling down the walk at a fast trot. She was wearing a skintight sweater and short shorts. Her breasts would have filled brandy snifters, and she had thighs like a wild mare.

Neither one of us spoke as she climbed in the Rolls. I gunned the engine with a brilliant touch of suggestiveness, my conscience plaguing me because I knew that I had done just this with another girl in another chapter. We roared off to our old parking place at Statuatory Park. And then she was in my arms, her mouth was warm and wet, and my eager hands were groping, finding, squeezing, caressing, pinching, scratching, stroking, unfastening, removing, guiding, tapping—and then at last relaxing. We lay back, panting, until finally we were still. The only noise that could be heard was a ticking on the dashboard.

"The Rolls-Royce people really ought to do something about that damn clock," Cashmere said.

The following evening I decided to stay at home to chat with my parents. I felt no further need for feminine companionship, as my date with Cashmere had the same lasting effect as six-month floor wax. She was all gender, that girl.

There we were, two proud parents and their successful worldly son, home to visit. Two simple country folk from Weedville, and a suave and polished young sophisticate from Madison Avenue. Two paupers and a prince. Two thorns and a rose. An observer would have looked in on us as we sat in the parlor and sworn it was the lobby of the Grand Hotel. But I loved them, and the sight we must have made.

Kicking off my shoes, stretching out in the old easy chair with the crocheted doilies on the arms, I patiently awaited the golden sound of their voices. People today do not converse, and an evening of pleasant exchange with my parents was, to me, a most welcome respite.

I was not disappointed. After an hour of silence, Maw said, "Nice to see you, son." About two hours later, Paw spoke. "If there's goin' to be this constant chatter, let's turn on the TV."

Maw and I leaped for *TV Guide*. We decided to watch their favorite gangster show, *The Unmentionables*.

This was an hour-long program, full of genuine thrills and excitement. But of course, the program is known to you. This one was much like the others in the series. It began when a small band of Italian federal agents round up a bunch of Anglo-Saxon hoodlums. The leader of the underworld gang is a scar-faced villain named Iliad Mess, boss of the Chicago rackets. The time is during Prohibition and Mess is illegally operating a chain of breweries that produce a beer called Mess Malt.

Everyone in Chicago is drinking Mess Malt and Iliad Mess and his gang of cutthroats are getting rich. So rich in fact that they are buying houses along the North Shore. At this point, in steps the hero, Al Capon, and his crew of federal Unmentionables. Al tries to indict Mess and his gang on income tax invasion, but Iliad cleverly soaks his accounting books in a brewery vat, making them completely illegible. Capon retaliates by filching the best of Iliad's coin machines, breaking it open, and stealing all the gum balls except the licorice ones. Iliad gets even by ripping the buttons off Al Capon's vest, but then Al steals Iliad's moll's peroxide and refuses to give it back.

By this time Iliad Mess is starting to get angry, and vows to get Al Capon for keeps. He goes completely berserk, grabs an ax and chops holes in all his beer vats. In a matter of minutes Chicago is submerged in fathoms of Mess Malt. There is only one avenue of escape for criminal and cop alike, and that is to swim to Gary, Indiana, and safety. Iliad Mess and the rest of his greasy Anglo-Saxon underworld hoodlums all make it safely to Gary, the grease being no handicap in a long swim. However, Al Capon and his clean-cut Italian federal agents, who of course are not nearly so greasy, are drowned.

When he hears the news, Mess throws a big party and everyone gets pleasantly mellow on Mess Malt. They all gather around the piano to toast Iliad, singing *For He's a Jolly Good Felon.*

Like all the programs, no matter what violence precedes it, there is always a happy ending.

"Boy," said Paw, letting out a breath he had been holding for the last fifteen minutes, "that was sure some show."

"Son," asked Maw, "what did you think of the hero, Al Capon?"

"I thought he was chicken," I quipped, my bright green eyes dancing with deviltry.

That was my one serious mistake. Paw's face grew black with rage. He reached for a handful of stones he kept in a bucket by the chair. Maw's face became red with anger as she reached for some garbage, left over from dinner.

"Mr. Capon," said Paw, winding up, "is a fine man."

"He's really cleaned up Chicago," added Maw, pretending to hold a base runner on first.

Before I knew it the old familiar sensation of stones and garbage striking me about the head and ears swept over me, so I made a dash for the Rolls and made my escape. Driving for a time in a fury, followed by a fit of depression, I suddenly began to laugh. I couldn't help being glad that I had gone home. Home to those who knew me and who loved me for what I was, not what I might have been. It was, I thought, removing a bit of pie crust from behind my ear, good to be alive.

CHAPTER 14

A tall, statuesque girl walked into my office at Pearl & Swine one morning. A slave bracelet jingled around each of her ankles. The way she slumped into a chair, the way she jammed a cigarette into a long holder and lit it by scratching a match on my desk top, the way she chewed her gum and casually filed her fingernails while I interviewed her, told me at once that here was a girl above the usual run.

I introduced myself.

"Pleased to make your acquaintance, I'm sure," she said, extending a hand for me to kiss, in a traditional greeting that is the stock in trade of the Katherine Gibbs girl.

"How's life at the Barbizon?" I asked.

"Like I say, Max, about as usual," she said. "The mad gay whirl of resort life, the colorful cotillion balls, the dancing barefoot out on the terrace till dawn, the cocktail parties every afternoon, the marvelous service from all the help, and foods fit only for a gourmet make the Barbizon the finest hotel for young women in all of greater New York."

Oh yes. I forgot to identify the lady for you. Her name was Lorna Layout, and in less than two weeks she became one of the best secretaries to ever fill the air with oaths while changing a typewriter ribbon. Once emancipated from the secretarial school and the hotel for young women, the rebellious facets of her nature disappeared. They were replaced with a quiet formality, a certain good taste, a charming manner, and an ability to produce great quantities of work with the efficiency of an automaton. She was, in brief, a jewel.

But the work on the Leaky account was endless. I took to getting to the office at seven in the morning and not leaving until ten at night. To those of you who work in advertising this may seem a short day. But heed: I also worked between twelve and three while the rest of the staff was out belting vodka. When top management found me sleeping at my desk (I was in pajamas) several mornings in a row, they deemed it high time I was given not only a secretary but an assistant.

His name was Gangle Acne, he was nineteen years old and fresh from the Harvard Business School. A lean, attractive teen-ager with a strong face well set about with just enough blemishes to give it character, he drooled whenever he spoke. But at least he was an Assistant, and you don't look a gift horse in the mouth, or give it a saliva test. Gangle became my aide. He pitched in with gusto. There was much to do. Here, his good breeding and splendid training paid off. His first responsibility to see to it that I was given clean pajamas once a week.

One morning as we toiled together, I asked him if he ever had any relatives who owned a costume rental company near Coolidge College, adding that I had known a gentleman by the name of Acne while attending there.

"Man," said Gangle, "that's my Daddio."

"Well, well, well," I said. "I knew your father only slightly, but I respected his judgment always in finding *the* costume for any occasion."

"Man," said Gangle, "that's the most."

We were friends.

At that moment in walked Lorna, looking even more crisp and beautiful than usual. It was always a joy to have Lorna enter my office. There were many reasons. One was a charming eccentricity of hers; she always leaned against me when she talked. It was not a conscious gesture as she was always hundred per cent business.

"Sir, here are the latest Nielsen figures on the septic-tank spots," she said, walking to where I sat and pressing her perfect pelvis into my shoulder.

"Thank you, Lorna," I smiled in genuine pleasure. "And by the way, this is my new assistant. Miss Layout, may I present Mr. Acne."

Gangle extended his nail-bitten hand and Lorna extended her pelvis.

"Welcome, Mr. Acne," she said, "I'm sure you'll enjoy Pearl & Swine. If there's anything I can do for you at any time, please let me know."

She was cool but polite, always the executive secretary, and ever correctly formal. She strolled out of the office with that wonderful walk of hers. After she had gone it was a full five minutes before either Gangle or I could muster enough irreverence to break the silence and speak. Finally Gangle could contain it no longer.

"Man!" he exclaimed.

"Hardly," I said.

As an assistant, Gangle was worthless for the rest of the morning. After lunch I suggested that we put the new art work under our arms, take the NY, Huntington & Hartford up to Seepage, Connecticut, and show them to the client.

"Man," announced Gangle, "trains are the least. They're for kooks. Old Gangle's got the heap outside; we'll motorola to Leaky Land."

Gangle's car was indeed quite handy. He had parked on the sidewalk just outside the building. It was a small foreign sports car, barely big enough to hold the two of us; we are both well over six feet. With the aid of several passing pedestrians, we managed to get inside and close the doors. Gangle started the single-cylinder motor and we roared off.

Heading into the Lincoln Tunnel, I reminded Gangle tactfully that Connecticut was in the opposite direction. I don't know whether or not you have ever been in a car that has made a U-turn in the middle of the Lincoln Tunnel, but believe me its quite an experience.

"Man," said Gangle, when we had weaved our way out of the tunnel against traffic, "that was a close mother."

"Don't you think you should drive a trifle more carefully?" I asked, still trembling.

"*Man*," said Gangle, "there's nothing to get shook up about. Not with these." He indicated the objects hanging from his rear mirror and on his dashboard. It was a mélange of religious statues, baby shoes, and fur covered dice. Seeing Gangle's collection of safety charms made me feel better at once. Anyone who believed in all of these precautions just had to be a cautious driver. I was relaxed all the way to Seepage and back.

Next morning found me hard at work again at Pearl & Swine. I had put in several good hours when I noticed that neither Gangle nor Lorna had reported in that day. Finally, at about eleven o'clock, Lorna made her appearance. She entered the office looking worn and pale.

"Man," she exclaimed, slumping into one of the big leather chairs, "what an evening. What a gas!"

"What happened?" I asked.

"Daddio, I had a date with your right arm, ol' Gangle. Didn't get to sleep until three A.M. First we take in a flick at the drive-in. We eye a triple feature.

"Then we stop at a roadhouse, the Juke and Jailbait, for a suds or two. He drags me around the dance floor for hours, playing his favorite song on the record machine over and over and over."

"What's his favorite song?" I asked.

"Some rock and roll bit called *Statues, Baby Shoes, and Fur Covered Dice*."

It should be mentioned here that no matter what else might be said of him, Gangle's taste in music was superb. This was proven by the fact that soon after *Statues, Baby Shoes, and Fur Covered Dice* became Number One on the Hit Parade. In case you haven't been to the Juke and Jailbait, lately, the lyrics are as follows:

> *If ya wanna be my baby*
> *Then ya gotta treat me right.*
> *Jump in my jalopy,*
> *Tear around all night.*
> *It's got ten carburetors*
> *And it really is nice*
> *Statues, Baby Shoes, and Fur Covered Dice.*
>
> *Do ya wanna get lovin'?*
> *Do ya wanna get hot?*

Be my backseat baby
And gimme a lot.
We'll be snug and cozy
As a couple of mice
Statues, Baby Shoes, and Fur Covered Dice.

There's a preacher
In the village
Who will marry us, I know
With no license
And no bloodtest
Let's Go Go Go Go Go Go Go!

Do ya wanna feel electric?
Do ya wanna feel warm?
I gotta a kinda crazy craving
For your adolescent form.
So jump in my jalopy
And we'll drag and get spliced,
Statued, Tattoed, and Fur Covered Diced.

Music available on request.

Lorna continued, "On the way home we brake at Statuatory Park and instead of making out he wants to wave at all the other sports cars. Finally another heap parks near ours and he ditches me for some babe by the name of Holstein. I don't know what she had that I didn't, unless maybe it was the biggest hogans this side of Bordentown."

Gangle did not report for work that day. In fact, he never reported for work again; that was the last we ever saw of him. But there was something about Lorna's story of the night before that didn't ring true. Her bloodshot eyes and somewhat softer voice hinted that perhaps good old Gangle just might have gone in glory. My theory was strengthened by the fact that not once all day did that lovely pelvis lean on my shoulder. Although a little hard to take, because no girl had ever given me the cold shoulder before, patience was a virtue.

Soon Lorna was back in her usual form and she quickly and enthusiastically gravitated to me like a degenerate to a men's room. Not having an assistant was rough for a time. Gangle Acne had been a bright boy, and was the only kid I knew who had left the eighth grade to enter Harvard Business School directly. He was one of the more mature nineteen-year-olds I've ever met, and despite a trace of callowness in a few areas, his valuable assistance was certainly missed on the Leaky Septic-Tank account.

But now Lorna chipped in to lighten the load greatly. Not that she could handle much of the work herself, but her constant loyalty and companionship was aid enough. She was always willing to stay after all the others had gone.

One evening, we both worked late. We paused for a smoke and a breather. She looked so lovely, standing across the room from me, that my curiosity could be contained no longer.

"Tell me, Miss Layout," I asked, my soft hazel eyes pleading. "Tell me frankly. What did Gangle Acne have that I don't have?"

"Well," she said, "to be perfectly honest, I never could resist a Harvard man."

"What a shame," I said. "I went to Coolidge."

"Never could resist a Coolidge man, either," she added, dropping her eyes demurely.

The record for the standing broad jump is fourteen feet, three inches, they say. My leap to her side must have smashed every record in the book.

"Lorna," I breathed.

"Boswell," she breathed.

In a thrice we buttoned up the rest of the work, and fell into each other's arms. As all the desks at Pearl & Swine contained pull-out beds, we were comfortably fixed. Then it was lights out.

"Well, Lorna," I said after a while, "this proves the old adage that behind every great secretary there is a great executive."

"Deviate," she giggled.

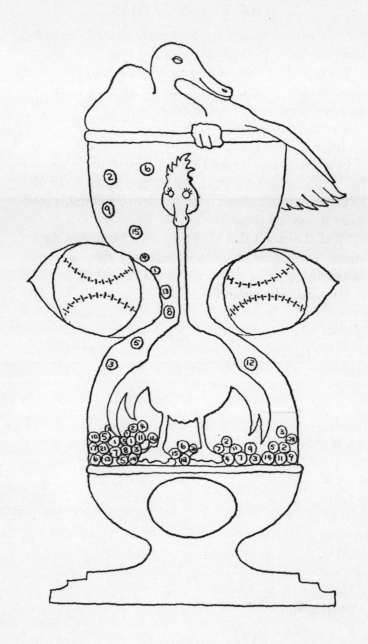

CHAPTER 15

Perhaps, as you read this, you might conclude that here was a serious young man who never escaped his business life, who never had time for sports and games. Nothing could be farther from the truth.

Like every active, reasonable man, I know the value of recreation. My favorite sports are baseball, bird-watching, and bingo. I can engage in them all with the deftness of a cat. Since those golden days at Weedville High, my interest in baseball has burned brightly. Despite Mel Allen, I'm a Yankee fan and attended a game at Yankee Stadium just last Saturday to watch my favorite player, Yogi Yogurt. I've aways felt especially close to Yogi for a strange yet wonderful reason: he looks so much like Mother. Those soft pleading eyes, that solid brow, that patrician snout, that proud arrogant chin, the absence of a neck—why, one would swear they were twins.

Yogi, of course, is one of the greatest catchers in baseball. Every time he squats into position he sets a new record for something or other. But last Saturday, when I had taken a seat at the Stadium, removed my coat, and plugged in my sterno stove, I was shocked. Yogi was not behind the plate!

Unslinging my Japanese binoculars, I patiently scanned

the horizon in all directions, knowing that Yogi would never dream of missing a game at the Stadium. Just as I was about to end the search, I spotted a familiar blob away out in left field. With trembling fingers, I adjusted the lens and sure enough, there was Yogi. Looking more closely still, I could see that he was weeping.

There was nothing to do but step in. I raced to the Yankee dugout to rebuke Casey Stendhal, the manager. As usual, Casey was waltzing with a strawberry blonde, but he politely paused to answer my question about the Yogi shift. My talk was something of a tirade.

"My good man," said Casey, "your interest in my ward is most admirable, and as your interrogation has the apparent selflessness of good ethics, I shall pleasure in filling the void of your discontent. Mr. Yogurt, having outlived his usefulness as a receiver, has been, shall we say—put out to pasture. Out there in field left, he may relax beneath the shade trees and sip cool water from the babbling brook that flows by. He will spend his few remaining years quietly grazing in the timothy and clovers that there abide. In a way, our Yogi has found his Shangri-La, as we all must when our time comes."

"But—" I protested. He put a hand on my shoulder, and the great voice that once resounded like a Roman senator became hoarse with emotion.

"The furors of infield play," continued Casey, "created violent environs for Yogi, and we felt that *out there*, he may bask in the monastic solitude of his September years with grace and gentility. If, perchance, a fly ball is sent his way by an opposing batsman, Yogi may or may not choose to give chase. He will have an able young associate nearby at all times, who will assist him in pursuit of such baseball."

"Like for how long, Yogi and left field and all?" I asked. "I mean the duration of him and you falling out doesn't make sense, for Yogi being a great player and like that, and who's catching while he's in left?"

"Mr. Yogurt will remain there," said Casey, "until the time comes for him to join such greats as Tris Speakeasy, Olin Mathewson, Honus Razor, Rogers Peet, and Cos Cobb in that Great Grandstand up there in the sky."

Both Casey and I blew our noses, shook hands, and I skipped back to my seat. I certainly felt better knowing that Yogi was happier grazing out in left field. His tormented soul had at last found peace. And as for his tears, what could they have been but the sweet tears of joy?

Next to baseball I like bird-watching, which has certainly grown in popularity. The trick is to watch as many different species of birds as possible, some say. But as in other endeavors, I prefer to specialize. You may have your robins and wrens, but I'll take vultures any day.

Now there is no reason to be selfish or closemouthed on the subject. It is an activity with room for all. You may need a bit of instruction. If you have no vultures in your neighborhood, there are ways to attract them. Simply snatch a small child from one of the larger families in the community and stake him face down in the noonday sun, preferably over an ant hill. This in a few short days will either bring the vultures or the Board of Health. In the latter instance, stake down one or two Board members, who will certainly produce results. Most do-gooders are for the birds and the birds know it somehow.

Now that you have found your vultures, you'll want to raise and train them properly. Building a feeder for your vultures can be fun. Make it a neighborhood project. Invite everyone over after Church on Sunday (your minister will gladly make the announcement for you from the pulpit; ministers love to make announcements) and when the job is done, you can serve coffee and little cakes.

When your vulture feeder is built, the next step is to decide what kind of food to use. Seeds and bread crumbs are peachy for sparrows and chickadees, but vultures want something with more *body* to it. Finding bodies for your vultures can be a problem. But an easy way to find some is to look along the ditches that border major high-speed turnpikes. A fine time to look is right after the Fourth of July or Labor Day week ends, when the pickings are especially good.

Another handy source is your local hospital. A few young resident physicians earn only peon's wages and welcome the chance to sneak a body out the back door to you for the right price.

Your undertaker is, to be sure, another friendly reservoir. Closed-coffin funerals are much in vogue today. Lead weights will be used in the coffin and easily fool the unsuspecting pallbearers. (One undertaker did get himself in a peck of trouble, though, as a corpse he sold was a late Guess-Your-Weight expert in a carnival. The pallbearers, all in the same trade, detected a two ounce discrepancy, at once beat the luckless mortician to a pulp, and tied him to the Ferris wheel, where he is to this day.)

To be effective, a vulture feeder must be kept clean.

The vulture is an immaculate bird without which our parks, picnic areas and beaches would be filthy in no time. You've heard the expression "clean as a vulture" so bear this in mind when policing your feeder. A fresh newspaper should be spread out on the feeder floor each morning. Some newspapers appear to be edited for just this purpose. One would almost wager that the New York tabloids seem to be made for vulture feeders.

After you have attracted vultures to your new feeder, you may want to capture a few and tame them. I did, and my pet vultures have become the subject of conversation along the street. Especially among my neighbors who used to lie prostrate on their patio chairs and take naps. One of our vultures, Waltham Reuther, came home last Thursday with an ear. Much as I hated to deny him, I had to return it.

Well, that ought to be enough to interest you in vultures and bird-watching. The trick is to watch as much as possible and to watch yourself. Vultures are tough to find, but the rewards are many.

Last, but not least, in my world of sports comes bingo, a game that requires not only athletic prowess but nerves that are hardened fibers of tempered steel. The bingo expert is a cool, calculating individual, and right here, I'd like to overcome certain misconceptions that have grown up regarding this most noble of sports.

Most people think that bingo is a game for morons, simply because only morons play it. But this kind of circumstantial evidence is unscientific.

Bingo has had an exciting and romantic history. It was invented, as nearly everyone knows, by Sir Malcolm Bingo in the year 1066. In 1067, Sir Malcolm took an overdose

of Hadacol and ran away with a shapely burlesque queen
(Eva Epidermis, known as the London Derriere) and
left poor Lady Bingo to face the bailiff without a ha'-
penny.

In going over his personal effects, she happened to
stumble onto his new game, which quickly became a
great fad in the family. The Bingo children were not very
bright, as Sir Malcolm and his wife had been brother and
sister. This used to be very common in England, but the
custom was later replaced by socialism.

Well anyhow, bingo caught on and because before long
Lady Bingo needed a fast quid, she sold the game to a
retired British Army officer, Major Gray-Chutney.

Bingo made the Major a rich man overnight as the
craze gained momentum, and hardly an evening went
by that there weren't shouts of "Bingo" at the top of
countless Anglo-Saxon lungs.

Years later, as fate would have it, Sir Malcolm Bingo,
now a down and out drifter, was hurrying to cross a
street to escape an approaching carriage. A neighborhood vicar was having a church bazaar that evening. At
that moment, one lucky parishioner yelled "Bingo!"

Sir Malcolm turned in his tracks instinctively on hearing his name and was struck down and killed by the on-
rushing coach and four.

The good vicar was prompted at once to stop the game,
as death had dealt a blow nearby, in the wake of which
it seemed improper to continue the festivities. But the
parishioners would not hear of it. It was Bingo they
wanted to play come Hell or high water, despite the
fact a ragged old beggar had met his end before their
very eyes.

And so, as a few less-avid players silently dug a grave in the church yard, and lowered Sir Malcolm there to a final resting place, the air was filled with voices shouting his name but in ignorance of its significance—Bingo! Bingo! Bingo! It was as if the angels themselves had come down from the heavens, their voices raised on high, and sat before their bingo cards, waiting for his number to come up.[1]

Well, so much for sports and games and the like. You could think that baseball, bird-watching and bingo are rather dangerous pastimes. But all the various forms of recreation have their pitfalls, even the more popular ones. In fact, just recently one of the girls in the office, whose hobby was nymphomania, had to be married in a hurry. The wedding preparations were a rush job; everything had to be done in half the time. In fact, the whole affair was about over as I got there. The bride and groom came out of the church on a dead run. We barely had time to throw the Minute Rice.

[1] Bingo is still played today among the more obscure races and cults, even in America. Many religious groups use Bingo and other lotteries for raising funds. Cars are often raffled off, so frequently in fact as to constitute serious competition for the automotive trade.

In one celebrated case in Boston, all the Cadillac dealers got even. They got together and raffled off an old monk named Julius.

CHAPTER 16

What on earth could machines have to do with a life as highly individual as my own, in a business so heavily creative?

As you know, an Account Executive in an advertising agency has but one function—to keep the client happy. When the client pulls the string, we hop. When he speaks, we hearken. He barks, we roll over. He rings the bell, I salivate. All in all, it's a simple, wholesome, clear-cut relationship.

Lorna, my secretary, always assisted me in keeping Mr. Leaky happy. Whenever he planned a short sojourn in New York, Lorna would shoulder the responsibility of procuring reservations for Mr. Leaky and myself. Lorna's arrangements were always top drawer—the table against the wall at Sardi's, a penthouse suite at the Plaza, fifth row center at *My Fair Lady*.

Her other selections were of equal caliber. The young ladies we met at the Barbizon were lovely of limb and pleasing of countenance. Perhaps you can see then why I wept bitter tears when Management decided to replace Lorna with an IBM machine.

Tidy to the last, Lorna loyally transferred all of her acumen to data processing cards, shuffled, cut, and dealt them one by one to the IBM computer. With a lump in my throat I bid Lorna a fond farewell. She shortly returned to her home town in Kansas and married her childhood sweetheart. It came as a distinct shock when I read in the New York *Times* that her married name was McSperm.

Mr. Leaky phoned from Seepage and said that he was coming into town tomorrow. Would we please arrange for hotel and restaurant accommodations as well as entertainment? Of course, he phrased his request in the manner of a country squire, saying that what he was after was "grub, a show, a pad, and some tail." Someday, I vowed to myself, I too would learn to use the Fairfield County vernacular that stamps one as a truly sophisticated suburbanite.

With Lorna gone, I was afraid to touch the IBM machine. It had punched mé once, quite by accident, mistaking me for a card. So I paced back and forth in my office, dreading the morrow when I would greet Mr. Leaky with no accommodations. At midnight I was still pacing back and forth in my office, wearing a shallow trench in my Bigelow, when I suddenly looked up to see someone at the door. It was Rosemary Clooney.

Mrs. Clooney was a large lady of about sixty years who came every night to clean the offices. She stood there in the doorway, bucket in hand and mop over shoulder. Typical of her trade, a rag was tied around her head. One stocking had fallen down around her veined ankle, from which a bit of pink elastic trailed back into the hall. She was to me a lovable sight.

Mrs. Clooney had been like a mother to me since I joined Pearl & Swine. I saw more of her than of anyone else. With her keen insight to the feelings of others, she sensed that something was amiss, and, dropping her mop and bucket, she came to sit down in my big, leather desk chair. Taking me up on her lap and resting my head on her shoulder, she listened patiently as I choked and sobbed through the whole story. Occasionally she would pat my back or caress my brow with her toilworn fingers, saying "There, there" to sooth my nerves.

"Saints preserve us, Sonny, but it's troubles you've got for sure, I'm thinkin'," she said in a brogue that would have made Honey Fitz turn green.

"It's hopeless," I sighed. "Hopeless."

"No t'ain't," she said firmly, and, dumping me from her ample lap, she rolled up her sleeves, exposing her flaccid biceps, and waddled toward the IBM with her jowls set in grim determination. I watched dumbfounded as Mrs. Clooney flipped through the ponderous instruction book, her shiny red hands finally coming to rest on *Programming for Client Entertainment.*

"Let's see," she mumbled, "we'll try the alpha-numeric scanner. If the core memory capacity can accomodate twenty thousand characters per second, the volumetric constant should compensate for the peripheral collater, and the data-tel will allow for the diode-transitor logic. This is a model with independent modularity, with data prestored on a fast-access bulk storage drum, meaning parallel processing ability. The input-output channels give us eight core memory modules which means fixed-point or floating-point digits—right?"

"Obviously," I said, masking genuine admiration with natural executive aloofness.

She spun the stool a turn or two for the correct height,

and seated herself at the control panel. Her deft fingers literally flew over the typetronic keys, programming the IBM skillfully.

"I've been practicing nights when there's no one around," she said, grinning at me over her shoulder. "It's sorta like the spinet when ya gets the hang of it. The action on this one is a little stiff. I like the Philco 212 they got over at Thompson better."

Mrs. Clooney knew her stuff. She had a swinging left hand for bass that would have made Van Cliburn envious. The IBM clicked madly away. Lights flashed, gears meshed, wheels spun, tumblers tumbled, cards shuffled, data processed, moving parts moved, and before you could say "Tom Watson," a neatly typed confirmation of Mr. Leaky's accommodations was in my hand.

Mrs. Clooney and I joined hands and did an Irish jig around the IBM.

When Mr. Leaky arrived the next day I presented him with the usual sealed envelope containing his accommodations for his stay in the city. Grabbing the envelope and giving me a sly wink, Mr. Leaky dashed away, neither starry-eyed nor vaguely discontented. After he had gone I patted the good old IBM several times with heartfelt affection. It purred softly, and modestly released an "Aw shucks" on the out-put tape.

The next morning, behind my desk, hard at work, the mail boy brought in the morning paper.

"Good morning, Fatbracket," I said.

The front page had the usual, stories on the union strikes, riots in Africa, teen-age stabbings and plans to increase the Social Security Law to make retirement mandatory at age thirty-five. When I turned to the local news-about-town on page four, there was a picture of a man being dragged by his heels into a jail cell by six burly policemen. It was Mr. Leaky.

The copy read as follows:

Lester J. Leaky of Seepage, Connecticut, was apprehended last night by police officers of the 14th Precinct. Leaky was arraigned at New York District Appellate Court, County of New York, by Justice Albert Anastasia who set bail for the defendant at $10,000.

Charges against Leaky were made by three plaintiffs. The first was Omar Orange, the proprietor of Nedick's snack bar on the corner of Lexington Avenue and 49th Street. Orange, looking very Princetonian with a black eye, alleged that the defendant, Leaky, was unable to pay his check and that an altercation ensued upon Orange's refusal to honor Leaky's credit card.

The second plaintiff, Gus Gumseat, manager of the Théatre D'Art, 114 Bleeker Street in Greenwich Village, pressed charges based on the defendant's creating a disturbance over the fact that the film being shown, *Sunset Strap,* starring Kooky Sideburns, had no English sub-titles.

The third count against Leaky was brought by Norwin Nodoze, who is employed as a combination night clerk-elevator operator at the Y.M.C.A. on 34th St. Mr. Nodoze's allegations stated that Leaky tried to usurp control of the elevator in a vain attempt to smuggle a woman upstairs. The woman was wearing the defendant's raincoat and hat, but as she entered the elevator operated by the plaintiff, she tripped on her garter. She was identified by the police as Mrs. R. Clooney, an IBM technician employed by Pearl & Swine.

Following the arraignment for assault, instigating a riot, illegal entry and petty larceny, Leaky was taken into custody and is being detained at the Correction House, Municipal Building of Queens County. A pre-trial hearing will be set at a later date.

Putting down the paper, I cleaned out my desk, typed a quick resumé, said good-by to IBM, and handed my resignation to Mr. Pearl. He informed me tersely that exactly ten minutes before, Pearl & Swine had lost the Leaky Septic-Tank account. Apparently Mr. Leaky had been allowed one phone call.

Needless to say I did not want to leave without a last word with laughable, lovable Mr. Swine. Looking in on him, he was bent over the morning paper, opened to page four.

"Mr. Swine," I said, "I have just handed my resignation in to Mr. Pearl. I would just like to go on record as saying that I'm sorry that the curtain must fall on what has been a brief but pleasant alliance. The hours that I spent here, the friends I have made, will linger always in my scrapbook of memories. Despite the fact that Pearl & Swine has just lost its largest account, I know that it will be only a matter of a few days until another $10,000,000 account will fly in over the transom to replace it.

"I know your regrets are not so much for the loss of the Leaky business, as for the fact that a wonderful relationship between partner and junior executive has come to a close."

Blinking bravely, I smiled my boyish smile and tiptoed quietly out the door. I can't bear to see a grown man cry.

CHAPTER 17

After leaving the employ of the advertising agency, I decided there was only one thing to do—get another job. My abilities as an advertising executive had more than manifested themselves, and any agency would have jumped at the chance to hire me. But as my leanings had always been toward writing, I decided that a more creative field might better meet my needs. Man cannot live by bread alone, as Mother always said in her letters.

Having made the decision to write, it was a matter of several days before I landed a job. It wasn't much of a job, mind you, just the ordinary sort of thing available to beginners but if I planned to pursue the literary life, at least it was a start. I joined a large publishing company as Editor-in-Chief of their big weekly magazine, *The Saturday Post-Nasal Drip*. The *Drip* was founded during the Whiskey Rebellion by Benedict Brandy, who suffered from a sinus condition until he had all eight cavities filled. Since its conception, it had risen in popularity until it was the most beloved of the low-priced three. Ben would have been proud.

Being Editor of the *Drip* was a snap not only because of the massive talent I brought to the task, but because every issue, week after week, year in and year out, is exactly the same as the last. Each contains one cowboy story, one love story, one mystery, one intellectual article, and one interview. Thanks to the company's Top Management, a group of men who had died years before but had never been replaced, this editorial pattern was never varied.

Let's take the typical *Drip* cowboy story and look at it:

Saddle Burns at Saddle Wells
BY BOSWELL SPAVINS

Saddle Burns was long and lean and tough. His face was hard, bronzed by the hot Arizona sun, and whipped by a prairie wind. His horse, who resembled Saddle, had been whipped too, by the long quirt that hung from Saddle's wrist, bronzed by a hot Arizona sun. The quirt was long and lean and tough, and when in use it whistled like a prairie wind. Saddle Burns was a cowpoke clear through.

His horse, Radish, was also long and lean. And tough. He was also fed up. Life, to Radish, was just a bowl of pits.

Then the rustlers came. They frequently convinced Saddle's steers that they were lemmings and the steers stampeded into the drink where the cagey rustlers caught them in nets and canned them as tuna. But Saddle learned they went thataway and headed them off at the pass. The steers, after a few subsequent visits to an analyst called Doc, became normal and grazed as happily as old catchers in left field.

Life was then dull and uneventful until the weekly runaway buckboard was overtaken by the ever vigilant Saddle and Radish. That's how he saved the heroin, a clean and wholesome woman, Sarsaparilla Hockjoint. It was love at first sight as Miss Sarsaparilla was a typical girl of the golden west—long, lean, tough, and whipped.

THE HAPPY SADIST

Sure as shootin', it was Saddle's lucky day when he met Miss Sarsaparilla. But when he bent over to pick a four-leaf clover for her, Radish saw the chance he'd been waiting for all these long, lean, and tough years. A well-placed kick sent Saddle's brains flying across the mesa in six directions.

"Oh, well," said Miss Sarsaparilla, a girl who is nothing if not philosophical, "Win a few, lose a few." She drove back to town, married Doc, and lived happily ever after in a sagebrush hut reeking of formaldehyde. Every evening, she sits at Doc's feet near the fireplace, and reads Pinel or Jung aloud until he falls gently but deeply asleep. Then she sneaks down to the saloon and lifts a few with the rustlers.

A staple item in each issue is the love story; and here a resumé of one that conforms nicely to the formula:

Don't Say Anything, Darling—Just Hold Me
BY BOSWELL SPAVINS

Nostalgia Yesteryear sat at the window of the old house on Bascom Street watching the raindrops as they struck the windowpane. Her nervous fingers wadded the lace handkerchief she held until it was a soggy ball. Where was Yuban? Why didn't he come for tea as he had promised?

She stood up and walked to the mirror. Nostalgia was not unattractive, even though nine feet tall. The front door. Could it be Yuban, deep, dark, delicious Yuban?

It was! Enter Yuban Upgender, a jockey dressed in racing silks. He is carrying a long ladder, and apologizes for being late. He is dripping wet and looks like a soggy ball. Casting a forgiving glance, Nostalgia runs to the table in giant strides, and pours the tea.

"Tea?" says Yuban. "I didn't bring this ladder all the way down here in the rain just to rewire the chandelier."

"My mad, impetuous Yuban," Nostalgia laughs down at her lover, who is struggling erstwhile with the ladder, "no wonder Papá doesn't approve of you."

Nevertheless, Yuban climbs up the ladder to success. But during a passionate embrace, Yuban, who suffers from bad health and has a cough that would make Doc Holiday sound like Vic Tanny, has a stroke. Then, a tragedy. The ladder broke in the midst of the stroke which finished him off in mid-air.

Nostalgia again sat at the window watching the raindrops. Good-by, Yuban, she thought. Then she straightened up. Enough of this silly sentimentality. She has her own life to lead. She would still go to the Red Rose Cotillion tonight even if she had to dance all evening with Alan Ladd.

At the ball, Nostalgia makes a big splash and gets roaring drunk. Her favorite ploy is walking around on her knees, telling everyone that she's impersonating José Ferrar impersonating Toulouse Lautrec. She has proved that she can enjoy herself, that she *can* lead a normal and useful life, despite the fact she is taller than most.

The next day Nostalgia sits at the window in the old house on Bascom Street, watching the raindrops, with one helluva hangover. What a lulu she tied on last night. Her head felt like a soggy ball. But last night was fun, and she had met many gentlemen who, though short, seemed interested.

She smiled to herself. At least she had kept the ladder.

Next comes the mystery story. It is, of course, a serial:

Ashes to Ashes
BY BOSWELL SPAVINS

Trenchcoat Trenchmouth tightened the belt of his raincoat, stepped out the door of his office, on which was printed PRIVATE DETECTIVE in fluorescent colors, went down the elevator and out into the New York night. The rain had stopped, but the wet streets gleamed under the street lamps.

Just then a scream came from an alley. Racing to the scene of the crime, a corpse verified his suspicions. Murder! A figure moved in the shadows. It must be the murderer. After him, with a football tackle. Just missed him, but did get a bag of trash. Dirty hands, covered with soot. Another dive, another near miss. The killer had fled.

That was it. Trenchmouth tightens the belt of his raincoat and runs to a telephone booth, and dials a familiar number.

"Give me Lieutenant O'Malley. Hello, O'Malley? I think I've got your murderer. Just missed him with a football tackle but I managed to leave a black smudge on his brow with my dirty hands. Find a smudgy forehead and you've got your killer."

Pause.

"Not at all, Lieutenant. See ya around."

The next day was Ash Wednesday. Finding the killer was going to be tough, as folks all over town had smudgy foreheads. It will take days before anyone washes it off.

But the killer does, and that's where he makes his mistake. Lieutenant O'Malley, a fat, dumb, lazy but competent character, spies him and makes the arrest.

"Well, O'Malley," says Trenchmouth. "I see you've got your murderer."

"Yeah," says O'Malley, "we caught the dirty, clean-faced Protestant. I hope he gets the chair."

Trenchmouth laughed at the lieutenant's lovable Irish wit. Tightening the belt on his trenchcoat, he walked out of the police station. The rain had started again. He hated the rain. It made him feel like a soggy ball. And then the bullet smashed into him through the buckle.

The last editorial innovation at the *Drip* was the introduction in 1890 of essays by scientists, artists, authors, and other men of attainment. Here's a sample intellectual article:

Ventures in the Mind

Eminent psychologist, Dr. Sigmund Gestalt Ebbinghaus, discusses the psychology of the dreams of the mentally ill, and how their theoretical interpretation can be turned into fun and profit.

As told to Boswell Spavins.

In psychology, surely one of the most lucrative ventures is the interpretive overtones of subconscious adventure. But this cannot be undertaken by anyone. The study of psychology is a long one. For the first year, as I recall, all I did was learn how to spell it.

My specialty is, of course, dreams. Many patients have come to our lovely wall-to-wall carpeted offices at 430 Park Avenue (MU 8-5300) during my office hours of 1 to 3, in dire need of psychiatric help due to nocturnal hallucinations. Let me illustrate by several case histories:

A young student of mine, whom we shall call Rory Rorschach, had continual wild dreams about floods. The water seemed so deep and black it looked like ink. This dream upset him so that he kept spilling his desk ink in class and getting big ink blots all over everything. The boy was obviously disturbed. The treatment was a clear-cut case of sublimation.

I got the chap interested in blotting this ink in order to neutralize this flood image in his mind. Eventually, he went to work for a factory in Pennsylvania, and today, by George, he owns the biggest bank-blotter plant in Johnstown.

Another interesting case, a rather attractive young girl by the name of Melba Mesmer kept dreaming that she was the governor of Alaska. In the dream there was a fuel shortage and the only way she could keep everyone warm was to take turns playing ragtime on a piano with first the fingers, then the toes. Frostbite always attacks the digits first. Well, sir, I tackled this one by taking the dilemma by the horns, ha, ha. I prescribed real piano lessons as what we call normative discipline.

Miss Mesmer became a fine pianist, and got a job playing at one of the best supper clubs in Nome, "Upstairs at the Igloo." In almost no time, Melba was the toast of Nome. She sounded so much like Harry Truman that a political career was forced upon her. In due course, she was nominated to run for the governorship of Alaska. Her election was certain, especially with the help of a campaign song she had composed herself that bleak winter called *Button Up Your Ober-holzer*.

This last case is so interesting that I've saved it as a sort of psychosomatic dessert, so to speak. Into my New York office at 430 Park Avenue, 2nd floor, came a chubby, pink little man, bald as a post. He said he was some sort of prelate, a Cardinal or Yankee or something, at one of the big churches in the city. (Being a scientist and not a spiritualist, I don't know one from the other.) Well, sir, this here fellow had one of the worst cases of what we call in the field, transferential identity, that I have ever seen.

Neat and tidy in his personal habits, the poor little man always combed his hair and brushed his teeth prior to retiring every night. This entailed looking at himself in the mirror. Then he'd sleep, and dream repeatedly that he was the Gerber baby. You may scoff at organic disorders of psychosomatic derivation if you choose, but yet here was a mature man of 89 whose subconscious departures from reality had given him a severe case of diaper rash.

There were only two things I could do for this poor misfortunate cleric. First, plenty of talcum.

Second, his frustrations definitely proved he was in the

wrong vocation. He changed jobs, on my recommendation, and he is a happy fulfilled man. The rash has disappeared. He now manufactures a whole line of baby foods with *his* picture on the jars. He is completely contented and eternally grateful. Every year at Christmas time he sends me a case of strained spinach.

It certainly has been my privilege to address you in the pages of the *Drip.* My practice, on Park Avenue between 47th and 48th, is immense, but this opportunity to address a mass audience was irresistible. With the money I've earned, I feel more free to recreate. Every afternoon after office hours, I like to play with these two little steel balls I always carry around in my pocket.

Finally, the celebrity interview gives Mr. and Mrs. U.S.A. a chance to chat informally with the famous:

It's What's Up Front That Counts

Miss Gina Londonbridgida, British screen star, spreads her lovely life before us in the pages of the Drip. *She is interviewed at her home by that lovable old traveling reporter, Pete Martian, and her answers are recorded by Pete in his out of this world style.*

"Tell me, Miss Londonbridgida," I asked the glamorous English actress, "in private life are you really an exhibitionist, or more of a recluse?"

"Me modest girl very much," replies Gina in her thistled Shropshire accent. "Me shy, me bashful, especially mine navel. In all mine movies, navel always concealed modestly by ruby."

Enter Gina's husband, who has been out in the kitchen gorging protein, and makes a grab for her.

"Not now," Gina hisses, "company."

Then a neighbor drops in. It's Freak Snotra, the great actor-singer of Hollywood.

"Next time, ring a ding doorbell," says Gina. "Me and him coulda been at it."

"Ring-a-ding-yourself," says Snotra, or Snotty, as he is called by the members of his group, called The Group. "Who's this jerk?"

"This Mr. Martian," says Gina, pushing her husband away. "Shake hands to Mr. Snotra. That's nice."

"You a member of our gang?" asks Snotra.

"Mr. Snotra, do you prefer to sing or to act?" I asked.

"We gotta gang," says Snotra, jumping up and down and clapping his little hands, "and we're gonna have jackets with insignias and everything. Just like grown-ups. We call ourselves The Group, because we're all together."

"*Mamma* Mia, you leave Gina be for a spell," screams the star at her husband, who pouts and kicks a nearby beer can.

"You first started as a teen-age crooner?" I asked Snotra.

"We're gonna have cars just alike, too," he answered.

"So help me," mutters Gina, "if you don't keep offa you big mitts, me telephone police."

"Mr. Snotra," asks Pete, "didn't you at one time start a bow tie fad?"

"—and houses just alike."

"Santa Lucretia," Gina shouts at her husband, "that's it. No more oysters, no carrots, no olives. No nothing!" He hides under the sofa.

"Tell me, Mr. Snotra, are you and The Group planning to produce a film in common?"

"Yeah, it'll be common."

"Hey," says Gina, "you come here write about me, not this skinny runt."

"And motels just alike. Who you calling a runt, you fat— —"

"Well, Mr. Snotra, it was certainly both pleasant and informative having this chat with you, and I appreciate your giving me an intimate peek into life among the Hollywood stars."

"—and swimming pools just alike, too."

"Both you getta out," Gina screamed. *"Via! Via!"*

"Nice to have met you, Miss Londonbridgida, we'll be dashing along, as you English say. Cheerio."

Gina smiled and coyly snapped her thumbnail on her teeth at Snotra and myself as we left.

"Now?" asked her husband from under the sofa.

This will give you a general idea of the *Saturday Post-Nasal Drip* and its editorial appeal. We gradually began to eliminate advertising altogether, as it cheapened the publication somewhat, caused it to appear too commercial. Great progress was made along these lines. Revenues began to fall off sharply. Everyone was terribly pleased, giving me a free hand. In fact, ignoring me altogether. Soon, I knew, we would have a magazine which, along with the *Mackeral Digest*, could truly make America great.

CHAPTER 18

As you read this book, slowly, reflectively, sipping each thoughtfully written page as if it were rare wine, you may have surmised that because of my busy office schedule that I never really had time to fall in love. Nothing could be farther out.

Although I met many a fine young hussy in New York, none seemed to please me nor, to be candid, did I please them. I would date a girl for a month or two, we would part friends, and then when we met on the street per chance, she would pelt me with stones and garbage. It was sometimes more than I could bear, and many is the night I would leave a party thrown by my contemporaries and land on the sidewalk below. Part of the problem was my refusal to give my heart to just anyone. Until one evening I went to Greenwich Village and met the one girl who would change my whole life.

Tundra Fairbanks was as lovely a creature as ever sat on the floor at a Greenwich Village party and recited Proust out of one side of her mouth and played the oboe through the other. She wore a black beret, black sweater, black skirt, black socks, black (they had once been white) tennis shoes, black horn-rims, and black teeth. I loved her instantly.

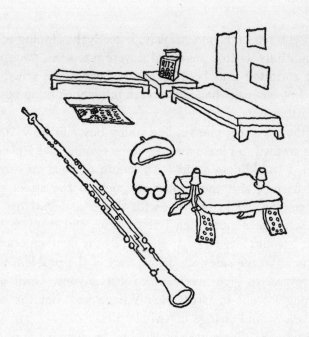

It was Sunday evening and I had just returned from an Ivy League week end up the river at Vassarine, a well-known college for women, where I had spent a wholesome week end with my date, Blazer Touchdown Gung-Ho. Blazer, a lovely little empty-headed flaxen, had given a party to celebrate her election as treasurer of the French Club. There were three hundred and fifty close friends of hers on a rented yacht. Needless to say after returning from a weekend with Blazer, who was one hundred per cent team spirit, I felt the need of a change. Therefore I went to the Greenwich Village party and met Tundra.

I asked Tundra where she worked, a stock question when you meet a girl at a party, and her response was most alarming. She smote me on the head with her oboe and informed me that work was strictly for the middle class. This is true, for neither millionaires nor derelicts work. So my next question to Tundra was what she did with her time.

"I contemplate," she said. "I digest, reason, peruse, conject, reflect, ponder, question, refute, analyze, criticize, deduce, postulate, deduct, analyze, criticize, deduce, postulate, deduct, and induct. I also make love with any man who will have me."

"Volunteers, one pace forward!" I cried, and took the giant step.

Along about Wednesday, we were both a little sick of it all. I had to get up for a drink of water anyhow, so I dressed and went to the office. But my mind just wasn't on my work after three heavenly days and nights of contemplating, refuting, and postulating with Tundra. It was an experience that was not only physically rewarding but mentally stimulating as well. I could hardly wait to return to her at day's end.

Sure enough, as I bounded up the stairs of that Greenwich Village brownstone the distant strains of a plaintiff oboe quickened my pace and my pulse, and sent my id thrashing about wildly like a caged beast. And as I got closer I recognized the tune. The sound tore at my heartstrings, for it was none other than the Coolidge College Alma Mater.

"For me," I cried, tears streaming down my closely-cropped cheeks. "She learned to play it just for me."

I burst through the door and will never forget the sight that met my eyes. There was Tundra sitting on the floor stark naked, eating Ritz crackers and cheese and silently reading "How America Lives" in the *Ladies' Home Journal.* Across the room, seated on a camel saddle which was the only furniture in the apartment, also stark naked and playing *Die for Dear Old Coolidge* on the oboe, was none other than Rabbit McSperm.

On the off chance that you've never seen a camel saddle, let me describe one to you. It is constructed mainly from four highly-polished boards about fifteen inches long, bound by leather thongs, and stands like a sawhorse about a foot off the floor. The seat is usually made of red leather and is fastened to the wooden frame by large-headed brass nails. For the naked, sitting on a camel saddle is not recommended as the leather and nails are usually quite cold. So naturally I was rather surprised when I saw Rabbit in his birthday suit astride the camel saddle in Tundra's apartment.

Never let it be said that I can't take a joke as well as

the next fellow, but I'll admit that here was a situation that could have put me on edge.

"Rabbit," I said calmly, after taking off my hat and coat and loosening my overshoes and tie (I always believed that a man should relax when he first gets home from the office), "just what are you doing here?"

"Well," said Rabbit, "it's a rather long story."

This was a pretty good start for Rabbit to think up on the spur of the moment because, as I'm sure you will agree, it's not easy being caught naked in a strange apartment playing the Coolidge Alma Mater on the oboe. But Rabbit was always fast on his feet so I listened patiently while he told the whole story.

"As you are aware," said Rabbit, "I graduated from college and married my childhood sweetheart, Lorna, who I believe was once your secretary at some ad agency. Well, you know my capacity for love making is excessive and my appetites dwarf those of normal men. On our honeymoon at Niagara Falls my demands on her person became frequent but not sufficient and one evening in the dining room of the Flynnlike Inn I began to itch. There was only one thing to do."

"You didn't?" I gasped.

"I did," said Rabbit, "right between the soup and the shrimp cocktail. The bus boy saw us under the table and told the waiter who told the maitre d', who in turn told the hotel manager who phoned Ed Sullivan."

"Of course!" I exclaimed, "I remember the night I saw you on his show. Yours was the act that followed the man who had taught an unborn human embryo to recite *If*, by Rudyard Kipling."

"Exactly," Rabbit continued, "and that's how I broke

into show business, moved to Greenwich Village and
rented the flat across the hall from this one. Our lady
friend here has been such a good neighbor. More than
once, she's bent over backward to make me feel at home.
And she is also helping me to be a greater success on
stage by teaching me to be less self-conscious, which
explains my nakedness. As far as the oboe is concerned,
I have to learn to play it for a movie I'm in soon. It takes
place in Egypt and I play the part of Nasser, riding a
camel after a band of rustlers who have looted the pyra-
mids. It's the first Egyptian western that Hollywood has
attempted.

"So you see," he smiled, "that explains my presence
here, and I hope you didn't get the wrong idea. You
can never trust first impressions."

Well, you can imagine how embarrassed I was for
having thought wrongly of Rabbit. Fortunately, I was
big enough to offer my hand in a sincere apology. It
seemed good to feel the old fraternity grip once more.

"But what about Lorna?" I asked.

"Oh, her," said Rabbit. "She's still under the table at
the Inn. Never did get up the nerve to come out. But
that's enough about me. What have you been doing all
these years since our golden days together at Coolidge?"

"I went into advertising at Pearl & Swine, and later
became the Editor of the *Saturday Post-Nasal Drip*. I
happened to attend a party here in the Village last
Sunday evening and that's where I met Tundra Fairbanks."

"Tundra Fairbanks? Who the hell is that?"

"I refer to the lovely lady who sits nude in yonder

corner eating Ritz crackers and reading the *Ladies' Home Journal.*" I pointed at Tundra.

At that point I thought Rabbit would die laughing. He almost fell off the camel saddle.

"Hey," said Rabbit, "this has gone far enough. Take off the wig, honey, and tell him who you really are!"

The woman I had known and loved as "Tundra Fairbanks" said, "Oh, what the deuce. He'll find out anyhow sooner or later." And with that she took off her raven black hair, the hair that I had run my fingers through and had caressed so tenderly, and there, stark naked, sitting on the floor eating Ritz crackers, was Mother Gabor.

"Mother Gabor!" I said weakly, "it's really you. But I thought you were still back at dear old Coolidge serving as house mother for the Gamma Rays. What in heaven's name are you doing in New York living in a cold-water flat on Christopher Street?"

"Well," said Mother Gabor, "it's a long story."

Without waiting to hear Mother Gabor's story, I proudly buckled my overshoes, straightened my tie, put on my hat and coat, and stormed out of the apartment into the cold December night. If I learned anything at all in my brief association in the Village, it was this: Never trust a black-toothed, cracker-eating house mother who reads the *Ladies' Home Journal,* owns a camel saddle, and plays the oboe.

CHAPTER 19

After a time, as the editor of the *Drip*, I decided that a complete face-lifting was what the old magazine needed. This could be accomplished editorially by replacing the old, tired sameness with a brilliant new style of prose. To set the standard, I personally submitted much of my own writing to the Board of Editors, being careful, however, to first remove any yellowing rejection slips from the editors of other magazines whose limited vision had prevented their publication. It seemed prudent to suggest the stories as I distributed the paychecks.

So much of my material was perfect for the *Drip* that several issues came out containing nothing but stories and articles by the editor-in-chief. As usual, if you want something done right, do it yourself. This philosophy has always served me well, with a few exceptions. Perhaps I never should have tried to remove my own appendix. I had one devil of a time getting all the parts back inside and sewing up a botched first incision that was easily a foot long. But no one can be good at everything.

The finest article I wrote for the *Drip* during this period was about the vikings. The piece was rooted in solid historical research and its prose style was without peer. I had learned that history is never bought on the

basis of literary merit. These works are always pur-
chased by the publishers at the rate of so many dollars
per footnote. Naturally, my story was copiously docu-
mented. The first draft, in fact, was 260 words with
23,000 footnotes. It seemed a little thin on top, though
every comma was substantiated, so I did a second ver-
sion.

King of the Vikings
BY BOSWELL SPAVINS

History tells us that the first man to set foot upon the shores
of the New World, the Western Hemisphere as it is now
known, was Christopher Columbus[1] who crossed the Atlantic
on his good ship Ave Maria. Nothing could be farther from
the truth.

America was actually discovered some years before by
three viking chieftains whose names will ever be inscribed on
the pages of time. They were Prince Rambler the Valiant;
Pierre the Lucky; and Infa the Red.

These three and their band of merry men left the political
unit commonly known as Norway about the time of the battle
of Hastings[2] and sailed westward, quarreling every oar-stroke
of the way. They sailed to the shores of what is now Canada
and up the St. Lawrence Seaway, turning south onto Lake
Champlain. They landed at an historic point, Weedville,[3]
New York and were met by a tribe of friendly indians, the
Tapiocas.

The chief of the Tapiocas, Bluejaywalking, made them
welcome in his village. He introduced them to his beautiful

[1] Italian, naval officer, circa 1492. Married Isabella, Queen of Scots.
[2] Following which, the duchy was divided into Hastings, Nebraska, and
Hastings-on-Hudson.
[3] The birthplace of your author.

daughter, Spreadeagle, who soon introduced them to practices they had never heard of. The Indian princess was so fair that the three vikings were at once smitten with love. They took turns sneaking to her tent at night.[4]

But wise old Chief Bluejaywalking was not to have his lovely[5] daughter won so easily, and he told the three chieftains that they must curtail their nocturnal visits. He also informed his daughter that the three vikings were not for her, as the old chief had always opposed mixed marriages.

But Spreadeagle said she sorta cottoned to all three.[6] Wouldn't it be fun, the maiden is said to have said, to have a contest. Chief Bluejaywalking finally agreed and insisted on judging the contest himself. He informed the three Norway-wards of the rules.[7] Each was to submit in twenty-five words or less the reason why he wanted Spreadeagle for his bride. All entries were to be judged on the basis of neatness, originality, and lust. And the decision of the judge would be final.

As the charms of Spreadeagle were rather obvious, the three answers were pretty much identical in thought if not in word, and wise old Chief Bluejaywalking couldn't stop blushing as he read them over and over.[8] The manuscripts have been lost but the idea expressed in all three entries was quite consistent. Try as he would, the old chief could not make a decision. To make matters worse, winter was coming on and the nights were getting colder. Spreadeagle and her three suitors were anxious to have the contest over.

As time went by, tempers became shorter and finally Pierre

[4] The birthmark of American democracy, in action.

[5] 38, 26, 36

[6] See Elliott Springs Mills, *Sexy Advertisements and Divertissements,* New York, 1959, inside back cover.

[7] Bluejaywalking was a stickler for rules and fair play. When the English came to Canada some years later, the old chief was renamed the Marquis of Pillsbury.

[8] The contest was not open to employees or members of Spreadeagle's family.

the Lucky hauled off and hit Infa with a snow shovel one morning while they were removing the snow from the skating rink. Infa retaliated with a sharp right, in which he held an ax, to Pierre's head and the fight was on. While the whole Tapioca tribe turned out to watch the scrap, Prince Rambler and Spreadeagle slipped away from camp and were married by a friendly Justice of the Piece (sic). After a wonderful honeymoon, seven heavenly days and nights at what is now the Flynnlike Inn,[9] they returned rather sheepishly to camp.

Much to their surprise the fight was still going on. Rambler, great and noble leader that he was, stepped in and stopped the fight by suggesting that they all have a skating party. In a few minutes the rink was covered with vikings and Tapiocas, and the air was filled with the laughter of good sport.

Prince Rambler was a wonderful skater indeed and he whizzed around the rink even faster than the smart alecks at Central Park, impressing everyone there with his prowess. But poor Spreadeagle could hardly skate at all. If her morals were weak, her ankles were even weaker, and Prince Rambler was ashamed to have to hold her up as they tried again and again to waltz to *Dice, Baby Statues, and Fur*.[10]

Skating reminded Rambler of Sonja Henna, his boyhood sweetheart, back home in what is now Norway. She was a typical Nordic blonde whose flaxen locks flew behind her proudly as she sped around the skating rink in years past. The vision of her waiting for him back home was too much for the viking leader. He broke down and wept, finally telling Spreadeagle that he must away and return to his homeland to marry Sonja, because if there was one thing he couldn't stand, it was a lousy skater.

Spreadeagle said it was okay by her because if there was

[9] An interesting example of Pre-Mayan 109 architecture, done in semi-crib style. See also: *Masters on Modern Architecture* and *Sons of Masters of Modern Architecture*.
[10] Later renamed *Indian Love Call*

one thing she couldn't stand it was a viking who says he wants to make love and then never has a wrench handy to take his armor off. Cuddling up to ice-cold armor was no picnic, she said in some anger, and the sooner he went clanking back to what is now Norway, the happier she would be.

So, with a song in their hearts, Prince Rambler the Valiant, Pierre the Lucky, Infa the Red and all their merry men took off in their ship and left for what is now Norway, quarreling every oar-stroke of the way. Though subsequent diggings and carbon-14 dating attests that they made it only as far as Provincetown, they lived happily ever after.[11] Rambler married his beloved Sonja, bought a compact little house in a medium-priced range, and raised four fine sons, Corvair, Lark, Falcon, and Romney.

Spreadeagle also lived happily ever after. After dark one evening she silently stole away from the Tapioca village to marry the Justice of the Piece (sic). He and Spreadeagle later bought the Flynnlike Inn and while the ex-jurist served as chef, baking pies and torts and preparing his favorite recipes, Spreadeagle took charge of the dining room, made sure there were no honeymooners having a go-round under any of the tables, and extended her favors to any man who checked in. To be historically correct, it should be noted that the Inn was the first hotel ever to be approved by what is now Duncan Hines.

[11] Years later they sold an account of their adventures for a fabulous sum to a small but struggling publishing house that became the Viking Press.

CHAPTER 20

For some reason, probably the inhuman competition for ratings among the big magazines, I didn't last more than nine years as Editor of the *Drip*. The charge, as I was discharged, said that my policies were too conservative, my editorial selections too parochial. This was the straw that broke the camel's saddle as far as I was concerned. They may insult Boswell Spavins, but not the works of his pen, and not with anti-Catholic bigotry.

"I quit," I said fiercely.

"You can't quit," the Chairman said. "We just fired you."

Well, that did it. If they thought I would continue to work for them after an insult like that, they were crazy. Slamming my Begg on my head, I marched proudly out the door, my chin held high.

Yet it was only a show of confidence. Where was I to go? What was I to do? A feeling of despair swept over my being. And then it hit me. Of course—that was it! I'd write a book and expose them all, every last one of them! At the *Drip*, at Pearl & Swine, at Coolidge, back home in Weedville, all of the short-sighted everywhere who had failed to appreciate genius.

A book would put them in their place, if I could find

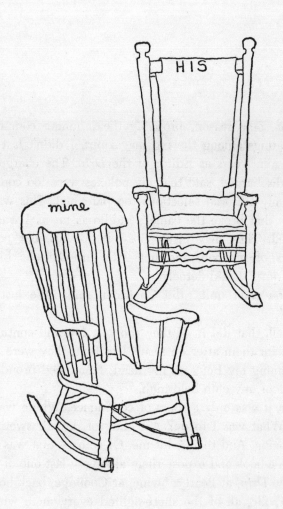

someone to publish it. But meanwhile, I needed first; time
to write; and second, a means of livelihood until the
royalty checks began rolling in. Making up your mind
is the hard part. I dropped in for a chat with the president
of one of the biggest advertising agencies in New York.
He was especially impressed with my resumé, and in no
time a job was created for me as Vice-President in charge
of Distasteful Advertising.

It was an opening that should have been filled earlier.
Their need for my know-how was appalling. To give you
a rough idea of how large my new agency responsibilities
were, I will list these accounts. You must admit that this
was an impressive group of manufacturers of products
and producers of services:

The Square-Toe Sneaker Co.
Saddle Burns Riding Crops
Farina Feed Stores
Hitler Wallpaper Co.
Weedville Chamber of Commerce (Travel Folders)
Manischewitz Wines (Paris distributor)
Vivisection Journal
Sonja Henna Ice Cubes
Yogi Grass Seed
Ash Wednesday Trenchcoat Co.
Leaky Septic-Tank Corps.
Unmentionable Breweries
New York, Huntington & Hartford RR
Spock and Crosby Childcare Books
Upgender Ladder Co.
American Federation Of Oboe Players
Katherine Gibbs Slave Bracelets

Flynnlike Inn Hotels, Inc.
Valleyforge Suntan Oil
Albert Schweitzer Mouth Organs
Cardinal Baby Foods
John and Marsha Tree House Kits
CBM—(Clooney Business Machines)
Acne Costume Rental Co.
Doc Holiday Cough Syrup
Minute Mashed Methodist
Bingo Games, Ltd.
The Saturday Post-Nasal Drip
Volga Plumbing Co.
Nasser Camel Saddles, Inc.
Lemming Raisers Institute

I was, of course, the obvious man for the job. If you're a religious person, you'll be convinced that it was manifest destiny that led me to a Vice-Presidency at Stone & Garbage.

I have found a home here. The creative men are pleasant to work with, despite the fact that every night at five o'clock they gang up on me and throw my trousers out of the window. The girls are all pretty and charming, and more than once have joked with me about the rather long scar that marks my appendectomy. But, all things considered, I am happy at Stone & Garbage.[1] Here I have found relative peace in a restless and troubled society. I have a large oak-paneled office with huge leather club chairs that hiss like cobras. My own chair, a musical rocker, plays *Die For Dear Old Coolidge*. The trophy wall has a large silver plaque, on which is inscribed the

[1] Formerly Stone, Garbage, Pelt, and Fatbracket.

first stanza of *If* by Rudyard Kipling. On my desk is a heavy bronze ash tray that has been known to shatter the teeth of those holding an opinion contrary to mine. My secretary wears a slave bracelet, with my initials, around each shapely ankle. I have, as we say on Madison Avenue, arrived.

My book has been completed, and has been accepted by one of the publishers here in New York. It is, in fact, the only publisher in New York, following the recent merger. As it is more or less the story of my happy sadistic life, we plan to call it *The Happy Sadist*, for lack of a better title. The title I suggested originally, *The Robe*, was rejected, capriciously, I felt. And so you can see, dear readers, I am at last secure. Successful in advertising, marked for renown in literature, my torment can at last sing bravely in self-expression. My sword shall forever cut in immortal brightness through a darkened world, cutting, stabbing, tearing, long after my wretched soul has departed to that Big Shop up there in the sky.

Respectfully Submitted,
by Boswell Spavins